Making Sense
of Cancer

"*Making Sense of Cancer* is a rich book—rich in knowledge, under-standing, and ideas . . . The author guides the reader through genetic coding, replication, epigenetics, and memes, drawing con-clusions not only about familiar concepts such as life and death and body and soul, but also about biology, artificial intelligence, and technology . . . He tells, explains, and opines in such an engaged and engaging manner that both laypeople and scholars will greatly enjoy the book . . . I was impressed and convinced and almost miss not having any objection to this tsunami of knowledge."

—**FRØYDIS LANGMARK (MD, PhD),**
Former Director of the Cancer Registry of Norway

"Breivik has written a very good and thought-provoking book, which should be read by both professionals and laypeople. Professionals will be able to see cancer in a much broader perspective—and lay-people will learn something completely different about cancer than what they can read in newspapers and magazines."

—**NILS CHR. STENSETH (PhD),**
Professor of Evolutionary Biology and
Member of the National Academy of Sciences USA

"*Making Sense of Cancer* highlights the multifaceted nature of cancer . . . Throughout the book, the author manages to describe and explain complex topics using straightforward language . . . Breivik dares to challenge the understanding of cancer, [and] sets the stage for a continued discussion of new perspectives that will help society make informed choices."

—**MARTIN S. AAGAARD,**
Journal of the Norwegian Medical Association

"*Making Sense of Cancer* uses humorous illustrations and simple metaphors to help us understand a very complex field . . . The good thing about researchers like Breivik is that he raises fundamental ethical and existential questions about what research is really about . . . Strangely enough, there is a reconciliation in this thought-provoking and insightful book."

—**CATHRINE KRØGER,**
Registered Nurse, Intellectual Historian, and Literary Critic

"When you start reading this beautifully written, broad-ranging, enjoyable book, you might expect to read simply about cancer, but you will discover that you are reading about life, death, and what it is to be human as well—because cancer is intimately associated with all three."

—**RICHARD SMITH,** former editor in chief,
The BMJ (British Medical Journal), and cochair of the
Lancet Commission on the Value of Death

JARLE BREIVIK

Making Sense

of

Cancer

From Its Evolutionary Origin
to Its Societal Impact
and the Ultimate Solution

RIVER GROVE
BOOKS

This book is intended as a reference volume only, not as a medical manual. The information given here is designed to help you make informed decisions about your health. It is not intended as a substitute for any treatment that may have been prescribed by your doctor. If you suspect that you have a medical problem, you should seek competent medical help. You should not begin a new health regimen without first consulting a medical professional.

Published by River Grove Books
Austin, TX
www.rivergrovebooks.com

Copyright © 2023 Jarle Breivik

All rights reserved.

Thank you for purchasing an authorized edition of this book and for complying with copyright law. No part of this book may be reproduced, stored in a retrieval system, or transmitted by any means, electronic, mechanical, photocopying, recording, or otherwise, without written permission from the copyright holder.

Distributed by River Grove Books

Design and composition by Greenleaf Book Group and Teresa Muniz
Cover design by Greenleaf Book Group and Teresa Muniz

Publisher's Cataloging-in-Publication data is available.

Print ISBN: 978-1-63299-761-6

eBook ISBN: 978-1-63299-762-3

First Edition

Contents

1: THE PURPOSE 1

2: THE BACKGROUND 7

A New Oil 7

A Failed Moon Landing 11

A Rude Provocation 14

A Big White Lie 19

An Enemy of the People 23

3: THE ENEMY 29

Malevolent Crabs 29

Multidimensional Warfare 34

The Difficult Peace 37

4: THE PROBLEM 43

A Biotechnological Conundrum 43

A Challenge to Society 47

A Personal Journey 51

An Alternative Reality. 55

An Elephant 59

5: THE CAUSE **67**

Smoke without Fire 67

Cancer from Living 79

Fading Flowers. 83

6: THE PRINCIPLE **95**

Darwin's Idea 95

The Building Blocks of Life 101

Selfish Genes. 108

In the Light of Evolution 115

7: THE EVOLUTION. **121**

Genetic Crossroads .121

Evolution Within 125

The Final Countdown. 134

Evolution of Cancer .138

8: THE SYNTHESIS. **149**

Epigenes 149

Memes. 154

Darwin's Theory of Information 157

Information in Concert 164

Levels of Understanding. 170

9: THE SOLUTION **175**

False Solutions. 175

Nature's Solutions .181

Immunological Warfare. 186

Contents

The Immortal Body 193

The Immortal Soul 203

NOTES 215

ABOUT THE AUTHOR 239

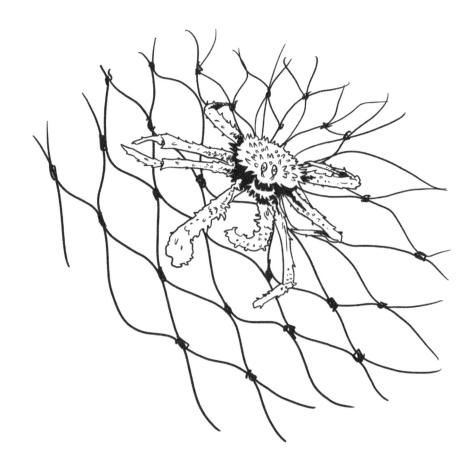

CHAPTER 1

The Purpose

CANCER AFFECTS ALL OF US in one way or another. This year alone, about two million Americans will be diagnosed with cancer.[1] Globally, the number of people who get some kind of cancer each year has passed 18 million.[2] Practically everybody has a friend or a family member who has either survived, is currently living with, or has died of this dreaded disease. There has been significant progress in therapy, especially for children, and it is important to emphasize that most people survive their cancer—at least in the first round. But being a cancer survivor can also be an arduous condition. Many people are struggling with lifelong late effects, and in the end, approximately every fourth of us will die of cancer.[3]

These are the brutal realities. We are facing an enormous and devastating problem of human civilization, and few things in life seem more meaningless than cancer. It is difficult to understand why our own cells turn against us, start to multiply uncontrollably, invade our organs, and eventually kill us. It seems both irrational and vicious that so many, even young people, get ill and die in this cruel manner. Why is that? Where is the logic? What is the meaning?

"Nothing in biology makes sense except in the light of evolution" is a famous quote by evolutionary biologist Theodosius Dobzhansky.[4] In order to understand life on earth, we have to comprehend the principle of evolution. In order to understand the human body, we have to recognize its evolutionary history, and in order to understand ourselves, we have to know where we are coming from. Only then will it be possible to find the meaning of life—at least in a scientific manner.

But is there a meaning to cancer? The question may sound strange. Obviously, the most meaningful response must be to get rid of the problem—or, as it is often stated, to find the cure. Surely, that is what cancer research is all about. That is what cancer researchers are paid to do. People want to live long and healthy lives without cancer. No one organizes fundraisers or donates money for someone to find the meaning of the disease.

Finding the meaning of cancer may sound like academic nonsense—a foolish distraction from what we really should focus our time and money on achieving. But is it possible to solve something that has no meaning? So far, we certainly have not been able to. We are constantly reading about new breakthroughs in cancer research. The cure is always right around the next corner. Yet every year, there is more cancer in the population. More people get cancer, more people live with cancer, and more people die of cancer than ever before. Something seems to be wrong. Could there be a fundamental flaw in how we understand the problem—how we make sense of cancer?

Cancer is often associated with death but is also very much about life. It is about the basic principles of biology, the intricate dynamics of living organisms, body and soul, tears and love, culture, politics, and money. Cancer is alive. It is something that arises and evolves within our body—a body that itself is the result of millions of years of evolution. To make sense of what cancer is and why we get it, we must understand where it comes from. We must find the connection between cancer development, the human body, and the origin of life. We need to look at cancer and cancer research in the light of evolution.

This may all sound theoretical and intricate. Cancer research and evolutionary biology are both large and complicated scientific disciplines based on enormous amounts of data. If you are not specifically educated in the field, it is easy to feel overwhelmed and intimidated. But the fact that something is complex does not necessarily mean that it must be difficult to understand. For example, we do not need much knowledge of physics and mathematics to understand that the earth is a globe in space, orbiting the sun. That is something we all learn in primary school.

The most difficult thing about this theory, when it was proposed by Nicolaus Copernicus almost 500 years ago, was to accept that it could actually be true.[5] People saw with their own eyes that the sun was orbiting the earth, and it seemed intuitively correct and highly appropriate to place ourselves at the center of the universe. The geocentric worldview was deeply rooted in religion and public perception, and the biggest challenge was not the scientific complexity of Copernicus's astronomical observations. It was simply to accept that everything could be completely different from how everybody imagined it to be.

In the words of Albert Einstein, "Imagination is more important than knowledge."[6] His radical idea was to change the perception of time. While everybody else assumed that the passage of time was always the same, he had the imagination to think otherwise. He showed that time is relative—dependent on our position in the universe—and most of us are still struggling to understand.

Things may be very different from how they first appear. That is also true for how we see our own lives. We are surrounded by living organisms of incredible complexity, and we perceive ourselves as something exceptional—as the purpose of it all. It can be difficult to accept that all this—life on earth and our own existence—have evolved spontaneously, by the laws of nature and the simple principle of evolution.

In order to understand cancer, we must be willing to view the world from a new perspective. Only then will it start to make sense. Not just why we get cancer but also who we are, where we come from, and what our future may hold. We need to see the world in the light of evolution. But not only from the traditional, biological perspective.

Evolution is usually related to genes and organisms, but biology has also given rise to the brain, our minds, and human culture. The theory of evolution is, in the deepest sense, about information. It explains how information arises and develops and can be used to explore all aspects of life. Even our thoughts and ideas—or memes, as we have started to call them—arise and develop through evolution.

Chapter 1: The Purpose

Genes and memes, body and soul, biology and culture are two sides of the same coin. Only when we see the different perspectives in combination can we truly understand the problem.

Finding the cure for cancer is a difficult riddle. And like other riddles, it is a deceptive question that misguides our thinking. We are imagining a cure in the traditional sense, while the actual solution demands a completely different mindset. Then it becomes both obvious and logical. Our propensity for cancer and aging is a fundamental aspect of what and who we are. We are mortal beings, and our technological pursuit of a cure has far-reaching consequences. We are facing an existential problem: Can we eliminate cancer and still be human?

CHAPTER 2

The Background

A NEW OIL

Some years ago, a neighbor asked me about my occupation. When I said I was a professor doing cancer research at the University of Oslo, he turned visibly skeptical. "Have you found the cure yet?" he asked with a smirk. "We are getting closer. Cancer is an exciting field of research," I replied as optimistically as possible. My neighbor was not impressed. "I don't think I believe in cancer research anymore. From what I can see, people are getting more and more cancer," he said with conviction—and, of course, he was absolutely right.

There is good reason to feel deceived by the promises of cancer research. Judging by what we read in the news, the problem should have been solved long ago. A newspaper article from my own country, Norway, may serve as an illustrating example. "Norwegian Solution to Cancer," reads the headline of a two-page editorial in the country's largest newspaper.[1] The article, which was published in 2015, is richly illustrated by the tabloid's legendary cartoonist. It features a nerdy professor, appropriately dressed in a white coat and small bowtie. Standing at the top of a ladder, he aims his binoculars at a dark and shapeless creature. The background is all red, and the illustration makes a powerful symbol of how our society perceives cancer—as a horrifying monster that only the best scientists can understand.

While the illustration is somewhat comical, the article itself is deadly serious. It explains how Norwegian researchers have made major breakthroughs in cancer research and how these discoveries form the basis for a new billion-dollar industry. "Knowledge will become the new oil," says the caption, referring to Norway's economic dependency on the export of fossil fuels.[2] The journalist explains how cancer research and biotechnology will ensure prosperity and development when we reluctantly have to phase out the offshore oil industry because of climate change. The notion is that the biotech industry will step in and save the Norwegian economy from its carbon dependency. We will stop climate change and, at the same time, save humanity from our most dreaded disease. It sounds almost too good to be true. Which is more important—to cure cancer, save the planet, or make money—is a bit blurry, but the article gives a clear impression that the problem is as good as solved.

The same article highlights a cancer researcher who made a particularly important contribution to these developments. Gustav Gaudernack is a retired professor from the University of Oslo, internationally recognized as one of the pioneers of immunotherapy. That is the new type of cancer treatment that activates the body's own immune system to attack and kill cancer cells.

Gaudernack's research on cancer vaccines has led to a billion-dollar company, Ultimovacs, which according to the newspapers is very close to solving the problem of cancer.[3] The company's web page says that they are developing a "universal cancer vaccine that works against most types of cancer," and as the company's CEO explains that "Cancer will become a disease that you die with and not of." What that statement actually means is difficult to interpret, but for most people, it probably sounds like nobody will die from cancer anymore.

Before we continue, I should disclose that I did my PhD in the research group of Gustav Gaudernack. I worked for many years in this exciting research environment at Oslo University Hospital and have made a small contribution to developing the so-called universal cancer vaccine. Gustav is not only a highly renowned researcher but also a compassionate and inspiring supervisor. He is the one who, with great enthusiasm, introduced me to the world of cancer research. It was also Gustav who encouraged me to go my own way and explore new perspectives on cancer. These are the thoughts and ideas that I am now trying to pass on to a broader audience, and it is with great respect and gratitude that I bring Gustav Gaudernack into this story.

At the same time, however, this book challenges how many cancer researchers and companies like Ultimovacs present cancer and cancer research to the general public. It is easy to blame the journalist when cancer research is oversold. Yet, few journalists have the knowledge and authority to ask critical questions to professors, oncologists, and experienced cancer researchers who promote their own agenda. Unfortunately, journalists often act as little more than enthusiastic and naive messengers.

Serious cancer researchers will never literally say that they have found the cure for cancer. But when they elaborate on their revolutionizing breakthroughs and exceptional results, they put words in the mouth of the journalists, who forward a message that lacks both nuance and realism. Then, when the media article is published, the doctors and professors shake their heads and blame the "stupid journalists." Yet, it is highly uncommon to see an expert who actually contradicts the sensational headlines. Most researchers appear to appreciate the positive media attention, and there are few incentives to explain what is really going on.

As usual, the underlying story is about money—lots of money. Cancer is a global industry with many different stakeholders. It involves thousands of researchers and research groups at universities, hospitals, and research institutes all around the world. Cancer drugs are developed by multinational pharmaceutical companies, and cancer treatment occupies large parts of the private and public healthcare system. Then there are all the patients and everybody who cares for them. In combination, they comprise an enormous interest group, which is promoted by powerful organizations. The American Cancer Association and similar institutions around the world set the agenda and form public opinion on cancer. They rally support, drive the funding, and lead the fight. The goal is to cure cancer, and there is little room for critical questions.

Why on earth should anyone be critical of the quest to cure cancer? There is hardly anything more unifying and honorable than the fight against cancer. It is the cause that everybody wants to support. People from all walks of life organize fundraisers and donate money. Children give away their birthday presents. We run marathons in pink T-shirts, and we let mustaches grow in November. Researchers dedicate their careers, and politicians compete to have the most proactive policies. Few things in life seem more important and noble than doing everything we can to fight cancer. What can be wrong with that? Do I really mean that we should cancel cancer research or stop treating cancer patients? Of course not. Cancer affects all of us. We can all, at any time, become cancer patients, and I am just as concerned as everybody else.

So why am I so critical? It is easy to think that the fight against cancer is only about curing a disease, but the problem is actually about something even more important and difficult. We are in the middle of a biotechnological revolution with far-reaching consequences, and the fight against cancer is the leading argument that drives and funds this development.

Life, the most precious and sacred there is, has within the last few decades become a hardcore science that produces profitable technology. Cells and organisms are redesigned by increasingly more sophisticated methods. So-called regenerative medicine aims to prolong human life, potentially forever. Serious and well-funded researchers are talking about "curing death," and we are in the process of redefining what it means to be human. Curing cancer is not just a technical problem of how to eliminate a disease. It is an existential problem that will determine the future of our civilization.

A FAILED MOON LANDING

The message that we are approaching a solution to cancer is eagerly promoted by sensational journalism and publicity-seeking researchers. But it also comes from the highest authority in society. Soon after the article in the Norwegian newspaper, a much bigger story appeared in the American news media.

It was January 2016, and President Barack Obama was giving his last State of the Union address to Congress. As usual, the speech concerned a range of important announcements, but one paragraph stood out from the rest: "Last year, Vice President Biden said that with a new moonshot, America can cure cancer. Last month, he worked with this Congress to give scientists at the National Institutes of Health the strongest resources that they've had in over a decade. So tonight, I'm announcing a new national effort to get it done. And because he's gone to the mat for all of us on so many issues over the past 40 years, I'm putting Joe in charge of Mission Control. For the loved ones we've all lost, for the families that we can still save, let's make America the country that cures cancer once and for all."[4]

It was a bold and positive message, and for the first time in decades, Americans had something they all could support. Regardless of political, ethnic, religious, and socioeconomic divides, everyone could rally behind the president's call to action. Even the Republican opposition, which had been instinctively dismissive of everything Obama had done during his two terms in office, was compelled to applaud.

The so-called Cancer Moonshot was the brainchild of then vice president Joe Biden, and the background story was tragic.[5] Less than a year earlier, Biden had lost his oldest son to cancer. Beau Biden was a rising political star, his father's pride, and only 44 years old when he died of glioblastoma, a severe form of brain cancer.

He left behind a wife and two children, and it is easy to understand that Grandpa Joe had an unwavering motivation to mobilize all his political powers to fight cancer.

The same may be said for President Obama. He also lost some of his nearest and most beloved family members to cancer. In a passionate speech about health insurance, he described how his mother struggled through years of disease: "She was 52 years old when she died of ovarian cancer, and you know what she was thinking about in the last months of her life? She wasn't thinking about getting well. She wasn't thinking about coming to terms with her own mortality. She had been diagnosed just as she was transitioning between jobs. And she wasn't sure whether insurance was going to cover the medical expenses because they might consider this a preexisting condition. I remember just being heartbroken, seeing her struggle through the paperwork and the medical bills and the insurance forms. So, I have seen what it's like when somebody you love is suffering because of a broken health-care system. And it's wrong. It's not who we are as a people."[6]

Later, in 2008, the day before he was elected president, Obama also lost his beloved grandmother to cancer. Her death, at the age of 86, was less tragic but still another reminder that we are all vulnerable to this dreaded disease. Obama and Biden's Cancer Moonshot clearly illustrates how the politics and funding of cancer research are intimately linked to deeply felt personal experiences. Every day, people are dying of cancer, and we have to keep on fighting. We are literally fighting for life—for ourselves and our loved ones—and as a society, we are willing to use all our political, economic, and scientific means to solve this enormous and painful problem.

Yet, there is something quite unsettling about Obama's announcement of the Cancer Moonshot. It seems like we have heard it all before. In fact, nearly half a century earlier, in his 1970 State of the Union address, President Richard Nixon delivered a strikingly similar message. Inspired by the Manhattan Project, which invented the first atomic bomb, and the Apollo program, which sent man to the moon, Nixon too promised that America should eradicate cancer: "I will also ask for an appropriation of an extra $100 million to launch an intensive campaign to find a cure for cancer, and I will ask later for whatever additional funds can effectively be used. The time has come in America when the same kind of concentrated effort that split the atom and took man to the moon should be turned toward conquering this dread disease. Let us make a total national commitment to achieve this goal."[7]

The idea of shooting for the moon to cure cancer is nothing new, and as most people know, things did not turn out according to plan for Richard Nixon. He had to resign because of the Watergate scandal, and his War on Cancer certainly did not solve the cancer problem. On the contrary, over half a century and billions of dollars later, there is more cancer in the population than ever before.[8] Every year, there has been an increase in the number of people who get cancer, live with cancer, and die of cancer. That is how it is in the United States, Norway, and most other countries. If the goal is to cure cancer "once and for all," we are certainly not doing a very good job at it.

A RUDE PROVOCATION

We are getting more cancer the more we fight it, and something appears to be fundamentally wrong with how we think and talk about the problem. We are faced with an enormous dilemma, and during my career as a researcher and educator, I have become increasingly interested in these questions. Still, engaging people in a meaningful debate has proven to be exceedingly difficult. The problem appears too big and uncomfortable to talk about, and as a society, we seem to pretend that it does not exist.

To address this challenge, a few years ago, I decided to provoke a public debate about the understanding of cancer and cancer research. I was looking for a suitable opportunity, and suddenly it appeared in the form of a generous Christmas present. Actually, it was the day before Christmas, and the Norwegian business magnate and philanthropist Trond Mohn was the prime guest on the national evening news. He was giving away one billion krone of his family fortune to cancer research, and the well-timed donation was quite exceptional in the Norwegian context.

Like most people, I am generally appreciative when rich people share some of their wealth for the benefit of society, be it arts and science or education and health care. Some may contend that essential welfare should be funded through a well-functioning, democratically governed tax system, and like most Scandinavians, I share this view. Similarly, one may argue that health and education should be a common responsibility, also at a global scale. It is difficult to understand why the development and distribution of vital vaccines should be dependent on the goodwill of individual billionaires like Bill Gates or Warren Buffett. If anything, the COVID-19 pandemic has shown that we must work together across socioeconomic and national divides to address global health problems. A virus that appears in one country may soon affect all of us, and we need international collaboration to monitor new viruses and prevent future pandemics. Anyhow, as long as the world order is largely determined by the rich and powerful, I am grateful for every billionaire who chooses to give money to cancer research or vaccine development rather than wasting it on luxury yachts, weapons, or ruthless exploitation.

One billion Norwegian krone is a lot of money, but the most conspicuous aspect of Mohn's generous Christmas present was not the size of the donation. The biggest surprise was the philanthropist's expectation of what would come out of the research he was funding. Mohn emphasized that as a layman, he found that modern cancer research is rather difficult to understand. But then he continued, "Some people say, maybe in 15 years, cancer will be defeated. This is part of the effort to remove a disease that affects every single family in the country, directly or indirectly."[9] It was an astonishing remark. Who were these people who had given Trond Mohn the impression that cancer could be defeated and removed by the year 2030? His donation was not an impulse. It was a well-planned and highly profiled event involving the Norwegian Cancer Society, major universities, and research institutes. Mohn should thus have access to the best advisers in the field, yet he seemed amazingly misinformed.

Every serious cancer researcher knows there will be more and not less cancer in the future. The statistics are openly available to everyone. In Norway, we expect an increase of as much as 52% for men and 35% for women from 2019 to 2039,[10] and other countries have similar numbers. Yet, the general message is quite the opposite. Almost every week, there are new reports about fantastic breakthroughs in cancer research, and as always, the solution seems to be just around the corner. Someone had to point out the obvious, and I decided to write an article in the *Journal of the Norwegian Medical Association*. Deliberately provocative, I asked, "Who Has Misled Trond Mohn?"[11]

The Norwegian medical journal is openly accessible to everybody online, and I was prepared for a heated debate with strong counterarguments. Instead, everything got curiously quiet. Despite my blatant provocation, nobody came forward to defend the claim that we are about to eliminate cancer, and nobody took responsibility for misinforming the generous billionaire. A couple of prominent colleagues privately shared their dissatisfaction with the article, presumably concerned about its effect on future donations, but in public, everybody kept quiet.

The only ones to comment on the article were two well-known proponents of the so-called Paleolithic or Stone Age diet. According to them, cancer can be easily avoided if we just go back to eating the same food as our ancient ancestors. The two food activists were not at all concerned about misleading the public but instead argued that the solution to cancer is simply to stop eating carbohydrates. Thereby they effectively derailed any sensible discussion, and my attempt to inspire a more nuanced debate about cancer research gave a meager result.

I had almost given up on my provocative project. But then, a couple years later, a new opportunity appeared with an even more prominent focus of attention. President Obama had just launched the Cancer Moonshot to "cure cancer once and for all," and the standing ovation reverberated from the US Congress and all the way to Norwegian newsrooms and research laboratories. Despite half a century of false promises, no one seemed to question yet another claim that the solution to cancer was imminent.

In my quest for attention, I decided to aim for one of the world's most renowned media platforms. I framed my message in the context of President Obama's State of the Union address and submitted an article to the *New York Times*.[12] The title of the manuscript was "What the President Should Know about Cancer," and somewhat surprisingly, it was quickly accepted for publication. After a few weeks of anxious anticipation, my article appeared as an op-ed in the prestigious newspaper, but the title was no longer my own. The editor was apparently looking for something more catchy, and the headline now read, "We Won't Cure Cancer." That was not exactly the point I was trying to make. There is an essential difference between curing cancer "once and for all" and not curing it at all, and I was worried that the readers would get the wrong impression. Nevertheless, my message reached out to the *New York Times*'s millions of readers, and I eagerly awaited the response.

It was not until the article was published in the newspaper's online edition that I really started to worry. The United States was in the middle of a presidential election, with Donald Trump as the most controversial candidate of all time. The publishing of my article had been postponed several times due to one sensational Trump story after the other, and the editors were apparently looking for a political angle to my story. And there it was: "Obama's Pointless Cancer Moonshot." My attempt to present a nuanced and pedagogical message about the realities of cancer had suddenly been transformed into a tabloid headline with political implications. I was hoping for a lively debate, but I had not expected accusations of being "just another Obama hater" or "an anti-science Trump supporter." It was a brutal lesson about the difficulties of communicating balanced information through the mass media. First, you must fight to be heard, then your message is distorted, and finally, you are bound to be misunderstood. I guess that is the price you have to pay to get attention. At least this time, it was not quiet.

A BIG WHITE LIE

Responses to the op-ed came through all channels. There were messages in the newspaper's online comment section, on Facebook and Twitter, in my personal email, as well as formal letters to the *New York Times* editor. The feedback came from all kinds of people with different relationships with cancer. There were researchers, oncologists, nurses, cancer patients, parents, and spouses, all with strong opinions about cancer, cancer research, and the pursuit of the ultimate cure. Their views were highly diverse and fraught with controversy, but in combination, they represented a fascinating window into what people really think and believe about cancer. As a matter of fact, the hundreds of responses turned into a small research project, which was later published in a prestigious science journal.[13]

Some people very much agreed with what I had written. One response was a personal email from a former head of the Radiation Effect Research Center, studying the aftermath of the atomic bomb explosions over Hiroshima and Nagasaki. He explained how he had personally experienced the difficulty of reaching out with balanced information about cancer and thought it brave of me to challenge the statement of the American president. He wrote, "I've espoused this point of view for 40 years and as you know, people absolutely hate it, calling it defeatist and short-sighted and somehow morally offensive . . . Although I admire President Obama, I cringed when he announced this scheme during his State of the Union address. Like the Emperor's clothes, pointing out the truth about cancer cures can be a bit dangerous. But it needs to be said."

The article also received the unexpected support of the cycling legend and cancer survivor Lance Armstrong. Having undergone successful treatment for testicular cancer at the age of 25, Armstrong famously went on to win the Tour de France an incredible seven times. It had been an extraordinary achievement, even without a history of disease and chemotherapy, and Armstrong became an icon not only for the sport of cycling but also for the cause of cancer. He founded the nonprofit Livestrong Foundation and toured the world with his high-profile campaign. Many people probably remember Livestrong's yellow silicone bracelet, which was developed and marketed in collaboration with the international sports brand Nike. More than 80 million bracelets were sold worldwide, and the golden band became the compulsory symbol for everybody who wanted to show their devotion to the fight against cancer.

In the fall of 2009, I was personally in attendance when Lance Armstrong promoted the Livestrong Foundation in Oslo.[14] The event was organized in collaboration between the Norwegian Cycling Federation, the Norwegian Cancer Society, and the Oslo Cancer Cluster innovation center. The audience included the entire elite of Norway's cancer research community, the pharmaceutical industry, health policymakers, and journalists. And the American hero delivered an impressive performance. The Lance

Armstrong Story was a fiery and emotional one-man show about the quest for "a world without cancer" and ended with a standing ovation while some discreetly dried a tear from the corner of their eyes. The fact that Armstrong was already the prime suspect in what would become the biggest doping scandal of all time did not seem to dampen the enthusiasm.

Seven years later, Armstrong admitted his doping fraud on *The Oprah Winfrey Show*. He was fired from his own charity organization. He lost his heroic reputation and presumably was forced to reassess his life's work in a fundamental manner. After reading my op-ed in the *New York Times*, he tweeted the following message to his three million followers: "Brutally honest article by Prof. Breivik in today's NYTimes. Certainly not a popular opinion, but I'm afraid he's right."[15] The man who had been the world's leading champion for "a world without cancer" had apparently developed a new and more nuanced understanding of the problem.

Some researchers who responded to the article took a more cynical approach to the issue. They accepted that there is no apparent solution to the problem but believed we should keep this knowledge to ourselves as responsible professionals. An oncologist put it this way: "We do need to drive the research, its funding, and the public health aspects by promoting the idea of seeking a 'cure.' That is a necessary frame of the issue to gain public support. The US public likes to approach these matters as a 'war on . . . ,' even though such wars cannot actually be won." Another oncologist was even blunter and said, "If aiming for a cure is what it takes to get money, what's wrong with that?"

Many people probably agree with this line of argument. A little white lie and creative marketing must be acceptable when the goal is to cure cancer. But what happens if this cynicism backfires? Large segments of the population are already distrustful of the scientific community, and social media is overflowing with conspiracy theories about the academic and political "elite" that deliberately deceive the public. In this context, it may not be wise for cancer researchers to tell white lies to get more funding, even if their intentions are ever so good. One thoughtful research leader put it this way: "The public believes us when we tell them that if they, or Biden in this case, give us enough money, we'll find 'a cure for cancer.' This is dangerous for us because sooner or later they're going to wake up to the fact that we've declared war on cancer a number of times and thoroughly lost each war. We should have said no to Biden, but it's quite clear that most of us are going to blush, take the money, and keep our mouths shut."

My point is not to diminish the value of cancer research. Research-based cancer therapy has saved hundreds of thousands of lives,[16] and I am not arguing that we should stop spending money on either research or treatment. But as scientists and academics, we are responsible for telling the whole story, not just the aspects that benefit our own agenda and funding. We must also communicate the difficult and controversial aspects, which some people may find disturbing. We have an obligation to put a critical spotlight on our own research. The typical way of "selling" cancer research is far too simple and deceptive. The strategy plays on fear, and the basic message is, "Give us money or you will die of cancer." The fact of the matter is that the better we get at treating cancer and other diseases, the longer we live, and the more likely we are to die of cancer.

AN ENEMY OF THE PEOPLE

While all researchers know that there will be more and not less cancer in the coming decades, many seem eager to spin the message in a more positive manner. The interest of the "common good" outweighs the public need for balanced and truthful information, and we may draw a parallel to one of the world's most classic dramas. Henrik Ibsen's *An Enemy of the People* is a play about a dutiful small-town physician.[17] Dr. Stockmann has discovered that the water source for the town's renowned health spa has been infected and is spreading disease in the population. The dilemma is that closing the facility will have significant financial consequences for the small town, and the doctor's attempt to inform the public is met with strong opposition. The mayor, who is also chairman of the spa, wants to protect the town's reputation. When Dr. Stockmann argues that the public should be informed about the health risk so that they can make their own decisions, the mayor replies, "Oh, the public doesn't require any new ideas. The public is best served by the good, old established ideas it already has."

Informing the public distributes power and may threaten the established order, and there are many political, economic, and emotional reasons why some people want to control the cancer agenda. A professor from Norway who asks critical questions and challenges the established dogmas about cancer research may therefore be seen as a threat. A registered nurse who responded by email put it this way: "You sir, are a jerk. One CANNOT fund Cancer research enough. Your piece in the Times conveys a stupidly 'holier than thou' attitude, based on self-aggrandizement. You've unfortunately had your say, now go back to nothingness in Norway. Eat well and exercise, and hope YOU don't get cancer."

Besides the high level of emotions, this response highlights a key question: Is it never enough, or is there a limit to how much of society's resources we should spend on finding a cure for cancer? Let us leave that discussion for later. It is said that all is fair in love and war, and few things combine love and war to a greater degree than the war on cancer. People are fighting for the lives of their loved ones, and anyone who asks critical questions is a traitor.

A PhD student at the University of California, Berkeley, wrote that my article in the *New York Times* was condescending and treacherous. An associate director of a prestigious research center argued that I was looking only to make a name for myself. Maybe they are right. I understand that my message may appear insensitive, provocative, and contrarian, but like Dr. Stockmann, I think it is an important message that is worth fighting for.

Some readers took the op-ed very personally. One cancer patient wrote, "So when I die of cancer at 38, because it's not worth curing me, will Prof. Breivik come to my home and raise my child?" Another wrote, "I want you to know I am very distressed by your op-ed. It read as cold, heartless, and uncaring. While this may be an emotional response because of my personal situation you have to understand that cancer is personal. It is devastating." I do understand that cancer is personal. I know that the disease causes immense pain to patients and their loved ones, and I understand that people get upset when I question the idea of finding a cure. I am humbled by the great grief many have experienced due to cancer, and I certainly do not want to hurt people already suffering. Nevertheless—or perhaps precisely because of these enormous consequences—I believe we need a more nuanced and critical discussion about cancer and cancer research.

That brings us to the last category of responses I received regarding the op-ed. These comments came from people convinced that the time had finally come that we would eliminate cancer. They believed that cancer research had reached an entirely new level and often pointed to the combination of gene- and immunotherapy as the solution to the problem. One professor wrote that "cancer technologies today are approaching the level of maturity that rocket science had in 1963," six years before the actual lunar landing. Another professor claimed, "If ever there was an opportune time for a cancer moonshot, it is now." And finally, my personal favorite came with a stinging remark: "Prof. Breivik sounds like a physics professor in 1890 pontificating on the fact that men will never fly."

He may be right. It is possible that some future cancer researchers will make me the laughingstock of the scientific community. I may become a legendary idiot, on a par with the technology leader who in the 1990s claimed that the internet was a passing trend or the captain of the *Titanic* who said the ship could never sink. I can live with that. What is striking, however, is that none of the people who claim that we are approaching a solution to cancer seem to have completed the thought and considered what a solution would really imply. They refer to scientific breakthroughs but do not explain how the new medicine will prevent more people from getting cancer. They point to extended survival rates and talk about developing a billion-dollar industry, but they do not explain how that will cure cancer "once and for all."

It may seem obvious that cancer research is taking us closer to the solution, but so far, the problem has grown only bigger. Something seems fundamentally wrong with how we understand the problem, and we need to take a serious look at what a solution to cancer actually implies. What will a world without cancer look like, and how do we get there? It may seem like an impossible project. But let us start by looking the enemy straight in the eye.

CHAPTER 3

The Enemy

MALEVOLENT CRABS

It was a rainy day in October on the Norwegian west coast, and the clouds formed a heavy lid over the grayish-green fjord. I was about five years old, and from my seat in the back of the old rowing boat, I had a good view of the fishing net my father was pulling out of the sea. Because of bad weather, the net had been out for too long, resulting in a vast web of fish at various stages of the death process. Some were twitching in desperation. Others hung limp and gray-eyed, while the fish that had been caught the longest had begun to decompose. It smelled like only dead fish can smell, but the most unpleasant was not the odor. It was the sight of several dark, long-legged creatures that had entered the net of their own free will. They were crawling the grotesque web like giant spiders. Eagerly hunting for food, they did not seem to notice that they had been pulled out of the sea, and instead of trying to escape, they continued to feast on the dying fish. "They are troll crabs," said my father, referring to the local name for the smaller cousin of the better-known king crab. A more appropriate name was difficult to imagine. The mythical moniker corresponded perfectly with the frightening sight, and the combination of fear and curiosity left a lasting impression on my young and malleable mind.

About fifteen years later, I experienced a somewhat similar feeling. I was a second-year medical student at the University of Oslo about to enter the dissection hall at the Institute of Anatomy. For as long as I could remember, I had been interested in everything that had to do with life and death and living creatures, and I was bursting with questions. How does the body really work? Why do we get sick and die, and what exactly is this *life* we are all so concerned about? Now, the day had come to literally face death. We put on white coats and were guided into a brightly lit hall with rows of shiny steel tables. There was a strange smell representing a mixture of chemicals and death. It was sweet and nauseating, but at the same time dry and irritating to the mucous membranes of the nose and throat.

There was a white sheet of cloth over each table, and we could clearly see the contours of human bodies underneath. My group was assigned to a large elderly man. Or, more precisely, it was not he that was lying there, only his cold body. A *cadaver*, we learned to call it in professional terms. Yet we wondered in silence who he was, what kind of person he had been, and what type of life he had lived. All we knew was that this cadaver had once contained a person who had made an altruistic decision and donated his body to science. We the medical students, our future patients, and society in general had every reason to be grateful to this man who no longer existed. He was dead, but his body and will were still clearly present in the room. Now he was lying there embalmed in formalin and ethanol, with a number tag on his big toe. Surrounded by a class of anxious and inquisitive students, he was ready to tell his last story.

We went to work with scalpels, scissors, and tweezers, and over the following weeks, we gradually worked our way inward to all the different parts of the dead body. It was a fascinating journey where we were constantly amazed by how ingeniously the body was organized. Nerves and blood vessels made their way along beautiful paths, through crossroads, around corners, and over barriers. The different organs were neatly organized, just as illustrated in the anatomy atlases, while the muscles and bones held everything together in an elegant and dynamic structure. The human body, and everything else alive, from bacteria and dandelions to cats and blue whales, are fantastic constructions. Life is amazing, and it is easy to conclude that only something magical, a superhuman intelligence, could have created something so complicated and magnificent.

But suddenly the harmony was broken. As we dissected our way into the thorax, behind the heart, and in between the lungs, we discovered that everything was not how it should be. The nerves and blood vessels disappeared into a shapeless gray mass. The same lumpy substance also infiltrated the trachea and the esophagus, and when we put the scalpel to this unknown tissue, it crunched as if we were trying to cut through a sandstone. "Is it cancer?" a fellow student whispered with anticipation, her eyes wide open above the surgical mask. As second-year students, we had not learned much about diseases but suspected that this could be the most dreaded of all—the Emperor of All Maladies.[1]

Our gloomy speculations were soon confirmed. The professor in charge of the dissections had access to the deceased's medical history, and it turned out that our altruistic donor had died of bowel cancer. But the records did not say that the disease had spread to practically all parts of his body. The original tumor, developed from cells in the mucous membrane of the large intestines, had grown through the gut wall and into the underlying tissue. From there, small lumps of cancer cells entered the bloodstream and traveled to the liver, the lungs, and other organs, where they infiltrated the normal cells and continued to multiply. Slowly but surely, these metastases had destroyed and displaced the body's healthy tissue. The cancer cells had grown wild, and the big man's organs had been devoured from within.

Advanced cancer gives associations to tentacled beings, which invade and destroy the body in a cunning and brutal manner. This is precisely why the word *cancer*, from Latin, and *karkinos*, from Greek, are both derived from the word for crab. It is the crab that attacks and kills our bodies. So let us say it loud and clear: Cancer is terrible. A few decades ago, cancer was, in most cases, a lethal disease. Before the development of advanced surgery and effective anesthesia, cancerous tumors could grow unrestrained. They spread on the inside, as well as on the surface of the body. Monstrous tumors developed into exuding and stinking wounds that would never heal, with death as the inevitable result.

An important example was the procedure known as radical surgery for breast cancer.[2] Such cancers, which develop from the glands in the breast tissue, was and still are the most common type of cancer in women, and until recently, it also was a highly deadly disease. The radical way to get rid of the tumor was to cut away the entire breast—so-called mastectomy. This procedure was first described by the ancient Egyptians approximately 3,000 years ago and became increasingly common with the development of modern surgical methods.[3] Unfortunately, however, the cancer cells often returned in other parts of the body. In their attempt to get rid of all the cancer cells, the surgeons developed increasingly more radical procedures. In addition to the breast itself, they removed the pectoral muscles, adjacent lymph nodes, and surrounding tissue of the neck and armpits. They had the best intentions, but the result was that the women developed severe physical disabilities in addition to the psychological strain of their difficult situation. No matter how much tissue the surgeon cut away, the cancer cells often returned, and many patients experienced the cure being more debilitating than the disease.

Today, things are much better. Most tumors are detected at an early stage of development due to regular X-ray examinations, so-called breast cancer screenings. Advanced surgery is combined with modern chemo and radiation therapy, and most patients survive the disease. The same is true for most types of cancers. Yet, many challenges remain. The treatment often involves immediate side effects, like hair loss, nausea, and physical and mental exhaustion. Then comes the late effects, which may include chronic pain, fatigue, attention deficit, hormonal disorders, and different types of organ failure. Finally, there is all the human loss and grief associated with cancer. Although most people survive their disease, the bottom line is that approximately every fourth of us will eventually die of cancer.[4] Even in our modern age, despite tremendous advances in research and therapy, cancer remains strongly associated with death and suffering.

Cancer is so bad that the word has become a metaphor for what we fear and hate the most.[5] In the media and everyday speech, we hear expressions such as "narcotics are spreading like a cancer in society," "the Islamist cancer is on the rise," or "corruption is a cancerous tumor in the global economy." Cancer is the worst thing imaginable, and to emphasize that something is really bad, we call it cancer. What we previously referred to as the work of the devil and the grim reaper, today we associate with cancer.

Let us therefore repeat it one more time: Cancer is terrible. Or to say it in the words of a slogan promoted by the Norwegian Cancer Society and other cancer associations, *"FUCK CANCER!"*[6] We hate cancer so much that even serious charity organizations use offensive language to express our anger. Parents of children with cancer wear T-shirts, and cancer organizations sell cute bracelets with *"FUCK CANCER!"* in capital letters. Why not? Cancer tortures and kills us, and it seems only natural to express our hatred toward the ruthless enemy. The anger is obviously justified. Yet, we may want to consider how this relentless hatred affects our understanding of the problem.

MULTIDIMENSIONAL WARFARE

The war on cancer is fought on many different battlefields. In the big picture, it is a national and international battle against a devastating disease that affects the entire population and all aspects of society. In this war story, the politicians and the major organizations of health care and research are the main actors. The primary focus of attention is to rally political support for funding cancer research and health care. President Nixon's "War on Cancer" and Obama and Biden's "Cancer Moonshot" are the big crusades. The Americans are leading the way, both rhetorically and financially, while all other resourceful countries are willing and loyal allies in this war against humanity's most dreaded enemy.

Like other wars, the war on cancer has its own propaganda, cleverly orchestrated by politicians, research organizations, and patient interest groups. All great wars need an unmistakable enemy, and our personal fear of cancer has been effectively combined into a collective hatred. Psychological research shows that to mobilize for a cause of action, the most effective strategy is to spark anger.[7] Aggression is a strong motivator, and war metaphors are a highly efficient way to gather political and financial support for a cause. It is a fight for good against evil, and the underlying message is that "if you're not with us, you're against us."

A somewhat different angle to the war story portrays the cancer researchers as the main actors. They are professional warriors and elite specialists fighting with high-tech weapons against malicious enemies. While cancer itself has become the symbol of evil, "finding the cure for cancer" has become the symbol of society's most heroic and benevolent achievement. If people do something brilliant, we compare it to rocket science or quantum physics. If they do something that is both difficult and compassionate, we compare it to cancer research. "It's not cancer research," people say to describe work that is somehow mundane and unimportant. Being a cancer researcher is not just associated with being intelligent. It has an aura of compassion and sacrifice. Cancer researchers are glorious knights in white coats who we cheer on to their next courageous battle.

This scientific battle is also about the fight between good and evil inside the patient's body. In this war story, the lymphocytes, a type of white blood cell, usually represent the good guys, while the cancer cells are the villains. They infiltrate and invade our vital organs, while the lymphocytes hunt them down one by one like the heroes in a computer game. At the game controls, we find the oncologists and the cancer researchers. They are the players who program and direct the lymphocytes to target and attack the cancer cells by using advanced biotechnology. But this game does not take place in the virtual world of computers. It happens on the inside of actual human bodies, and the role of the patients may be somewhat hard to grasp. In this biomedical war story, the patients are neither actors nor spectators. They are the battlefield.

That brings us to the last type of war story related to cancer. In this narrative, the patients take center stage as heroic warriors. Like the story about the researchers, the goal is to beat cancer, but the focus of attention is not just about killing cancer cells. It is also about survival, about becoming a "cancer survivor" who has won the battle and lived to see a better day. But it is also about the fight for the smaller things, like the struggle to get through everyday life, waking up every morning to a frail and hurting body, and getting through the exhausting and nauseating regimens of cancer therapy. It is often a fight against fear, against the unknown, and for many, it eventually becomes a fight against death. Then, when they die, the common phrase is that they lost the fight.

Barack Obama's grandmother, Madelyn Dunham, is a good example. She died of cancer two days before her grandson was elected president of the United States. Obama has described his grandmother as one of his most important role models. Despite racism and a difficult family situation, she motivated him to become one of the world's most respected leaders. Eighty-six years old, Madelyn Dunham had indeed lived a long and meaningful life. She had raised a child about to become the most powerful man in the world, and it would be fair to say that she left the world in triumph. Yet, the newspapers stated that she had lost. She had "lost the battle against cancer."[8]

THE DIFFICULT PEACE

Why is it that when you die of cancer, you *lose*? We rarely use such words about other diseases. This type of language immediately gives negative associations, and cancer patients and researchers alike have pointed out that this way of talking can be both degrading and misleading. Many patients do not identify with the war stories and feel a distressing pressure to live up to the stereotype of being cancer warriors. Society expects cancer patients to be active and positive, but that may be difficult, especially when you are seriously ill. What happens when the disease progresses, even if you keep fighting? Are you a loser who has not fought hard enough?

Research shows that many cancer patients are struggling with guilt. They feel responsible for getting the disease and being a burden to their relatives. Many have a bad conscience because they have not always lived as healthily and sensibly as they could have lived.

The fact is that none of us have. When other people expect you to always have a fighting spirit, it represents an additional burden. It is impossible to always be positive and combative. Cancer patients should be allowed to be sad, to give in to despair, and not to always keep on fighting. Various types of psychotherapy and motivational techniques may help you through the day. Still, there is no scientific evidence that cancers disappear or develop more slowly because of positive thinking or a fighting spirit.

Presenting cancer as a deadly enemy and cancer research as a war also negatively influence how people think and behave with regard to the disease. It leads to unnecessary fear and distress, even for the types of cancers that may be easily treated. The thought of cancer can become so scary that people suppress and deny critical symptoms, and many wait too long before they see a physician. To avoid these negative consequences, and due to pressure from cancer patients and researchers, the Norwegian Cancer Society, in 2019, decided to critically reassess how it writes and talks about cancer. "The Fight Is Over," says the headline of an editorial still posted on the organization's website. The article optimistically concludes, "As we all become more enlightened, we can also hope that we dare to be more precise and fine-tuned in how we talk about cancer."[9]

A similar change of perspective can be seen in the Livestrong Foundation, the American nonprofit cancer organization established by the previously mentioned Lance Armstrong. When it started, the vision was "a world without cancer," thus explicitly aiming to eliminate the disease. Today, the Livestrong Foundation focuses on helping cancer patients cope with their disease and the related everyday challenges: "We have a Mission Question, not a

Mission Statement, because we believe that we can only achieve the best solutions through asking the right questions. We ask survivors and caregivers what they need, we ask the system how it can be more person-centered, we ask innovators how we can bring impossible ideas to life."[10] Based on a deeper understanding of the problem, the organization has transformed itself from a self-confident war campaigner to an inquisitive and humanistic helper.

Despite these developments toward a more nuanced perspective on cancer, the war goes on. The American Cancer Society still "fights for a world without cancer," and new initiatives and organizations outcompete one another to be the most relentless warriors. A new social network for cancer patients has, without reservation, named itself "War on Cancer."[11] It appears that the negative implications of war metaphors have not reached the young entrepreneurs. The War on Cancer app allows cancer patients to share their medical histories in the open network. The goal is to "radically improve the mental health of everyone affected by cancer." How cancer patients' psychological problems will improve by sharing sensitive health information on the internet is unclear, but a closer look reveals the underlying business model. Like other social networks, War on Cancer aims to harvest and capitalize on its members' personal data. The cancer patients are encouraged to renounce their privacy under the pretext of contributing to the fight against cancer. And in the background, Microsoft and leading drug manufacturers are keen allies on "the digital battlefield."[12]

The war on cancer is in many aspects similar to the fights we have with other declared enemies of society, like the war on terror and the war on drugs. Killing terrorists sends powerful signals and may accomplish short-term gains, but it also creates more hatred, more poverty, and more fundamentalists. Similarly, we are slowly learning that incarcerating and marginalizing drug addicts only exacerbates the underlying psychological and social problems. War may be a necessary evil, but it is not the solution—neither to terrorism nor drug addiction, and it is definitely not the solution to cancer.

Framing cancer as an evil enemy is effective propaganda. It is easy to communicate, and it rallies support and funding for the good cause. But it is not very useful if our goal is to understand the problem. It is difficult to understand something you fear and hate. How do you get to know a monster you aim to eliminate from the face of the earth? If we really want to understand the problem, we must recognize that cancer is not evil. It is not a dark force that is out to get us. It is a consequence of natural biological processes, and the solution to the problem lies in understanding the underlying causes.

Amalie Skram, a famous Norwegian author and feminist, said it like this: "I have never portrayed evil because I have never encountered it in my path. What superficial and indoctrinated people calls evil are, to me, necessities and results. If I ever had a purpose with my writing, it was to bring someone to understand, to see and judge mildly."[13] Skram's writing explores how we are shaped by both inheritance and environment, and her naturalistic perspective on life is also relevant to the understanding of disease.

Although cancer has caused immense grief and pain, it is not evil. It is the result of natural, understandable, and often unavoidable processes. If we want to understand cancer, we need to see beyond the fearful monster. It is time to end the war and approach the problem from a new and unbiased perspective.

CHAPTER 4

The Problem

A BIOTECHNOLOGICAL CONUNDRUM

So what exactly is cancer? Let us start by approaching the issue the way we usually solve problems in our age and time: We *google*. Then we often end up on Wikipedia, where we can read that "cancer is a group of diseases involving abnormal cell growth with the potential to invade or spread to other parts of the body."[1] According to *Encyclopedia Britannica*, cancer is a "group of more than 100 distinct diseases characterized by the uncontrolled growth of abnormal cells in the body."[2] Cancer is also called *malignant neoplasm*, which translated from Latin, means "bad new growth." So in simple words, cancer is cells in the body that are out of control. These cells multiply and spread, seemingly without purpose. They create chaos and eventually destroy the organism from within.

Our cells normally divide and multiply only when the body needs them, for example to renew the skin or close a wound. Just imagine how the body detects and repairs a cut on a finger. Almost immediately, the small platelets circulating in the blood react by lumping together to stop the bleeding. Then, during the first few days, different types of cells flow into the wound. The so-called *macrophages*, which literally means "big eaters," crawl around and clean up the injured site. They eat the destroyed cells, as well as bacteria and foreign debris that may have penetrated the skin. Next, the *angiocytes*, which make new blood vessels, and the *keratinocytes*, which form the top layer of skin, begin to multiply. Finally, after approximately three weeks, the wound is completely healed, and the *fibrocytes*, which make up the connective tissue, stretch out and ensure that everything becomes smooth and nice, leaving just a minor scar.

The cells of the body work together as a well-functioning team, where the various team members have specific skills and tasks. This teamwork is carefully regulated through a complex system of communication between the different cells and organs. They send and receive a wide range of chemical signals, and thereby they respond, adapt, and coordinate to the overall needs of the body. In the same way that humans communicate with words that travel as sound waves through the air, cells communicate using molecules that float around the body. Specific molecules, which are secreted from some cells, bind to antennas—or receptors—on other cells. This connection then starts a chain reaction that makes the cells react in a certain manner. Some may start to produce a particular substance, while others begin to move or transform their shape. Most importantly, some molecular signals tell the cells to divide and multiply, while others make them stop.

When some cells divide to make more cells, others must die to maintain the balance. Otherwise, there will quickly become too many cells in the same place, and we get a lump, or a tumor, as it is called in medical terms. While new cells appear, old ones die. In fact, there are molecular signals and mechanisms that tell cells to commit suicide when they are no longer needed. *Apoptosis* it is called when cells deliberately die and disintegrate to make room for other cells. The process is somewhat similar to how soldier ants sacrifice themselves so the queen and the rest of the colony can keep on living.

This self-sacrificing behavior of our cells ensures that the body gets rid of unnecessary cells and is especially important in the earliest stages of development. That, for example, is how our fingers are formed. What initially looks like a small paddle or flipper becomes five perfect fingers because the cells located where the spaces should be sacrifice themselves and die on command. These cells have antennas that receive physical and chemical signals from the environment, which then trigger a biochemical computer program stored in the genes. Such genetic programs regulate all the various processes in the body, from digestion and sexuality to brain activity and muscle function. Everything is connected to everything, and the cells are programmed to work together to make the body function as an integrated unit.

That, however, is not the case for the so-called *neoplastic* cells. Such cells have acquired a new ability to multiply regardless of the body's signals to stop. They do not adjust their growth to the needs of the organism but instead develop into a tumor, which has no purpose to the body. Some tumors grow only locally where they first appear and do not penetrate the surrounding tissue. Take, for example, a regular mole or a lump of fat cells—a lipoma—that many people can feel under the skin. Such *benign* tumors usually do little harm; unless they are located deep in the brain, or other vital organs, they are normally easy to remove by surgery.

Actual cancer cells, on the other hand, are not constrained to a specific location. They infiltrate the surrounding tissues and send offshoots, known as *metastases*, to other parts of the body. They multiply without boundaries, and unless they are stopped by force, they will continue to invade new areas of the organism. Sooner or later, they will kill us. These are the *malignant* tumors—the cancers. Notice also how the language of good and evil—benign and malignant—has made its way to the medical connotations of tumors.

If we read on in textbooks or encyclopedias, we learn that there are many different forms of cancer, related to all the various organs and cell types of the body. Skin cancer, for example, can be divided into three main types depending on whether it has developed from basal cells, squamous cells, or mole cells. Of these, mole cancer, commonly referred to as *malignant melanoma*, is by far the most deadly. The other two used to be dangerous but are today relatively easy to treat if detected at an early stage of development. In the other organs, it is quite similar. From the intestines and bladder to the brain and blood system, different cell types produce different types of cancer. Some are common, while others are rare. Some are aggressive and fast-growing, while others grow very slowly. We have developed effective treatments against some, while others still remain highly lethal. Cancer is a complex phenomenon, but in principle, it is pretty simple. Cancers are cells from somewhere in the body that multiply uncontrollably without attention to the signals and needs of the rest of the organism.

If we ask cancer researchers who work with cells in a laboratory, we will probably get a similar answer to what we find in the encyclopedias, but they also have much more to tell. Cancer is a scientific problem and a technological challenge that they are trying to solve. Or, more precisely, there is not just one problem. Cancer research involves an endless series of small and large issues that need to be meticulously explored and clarified. Then, if you are lucky, you may find a piece of the big puzzle that can contribute to better treatment for one or more types of cancers.

Today, cancer research is often about finding patterns and connections in the complex world of molecules that float around and communicate within and between the cells. Each cell is almost incomprehensibly complicated, and modern cancer research is increasingly about using advanced biotechnology, supercomputers, and artificial intelligence to analyze and simulate this world of molecules. New discoveries are made every day, but contrary to how cancer research is presented in the media, few cancer researchers believe that they are about to cure cancer once and for all.

A CHALLENGE TO SOCIETY

Cancer research involves the study of molecules, cells, and organisms to find possible cures, but it is also about much more. Contrary to what people may think, many cancer researchers are not working to find a cure. For example, while some search for better ways to detect new cases, others try to figure out how to prevent the disease. Cancer epidemiologists study how different types of cancer affect different groups of people. They keep statistics on how many people get, live with, and die from various cancers. Then they follow the development over time.

In that sense, cancer is a disease and a cause of death, like many others. Yet cancer is in a class of its own. Not only because it is perceived as particularly scary but also because it is increasingly more common. Using Norway, a highly developed country, as an example, cancer has become the most common cause of death, pushing cardiovascular diseases to second place.[3] Similar developments are seen all over the world. As medical science has become better at regulating blood pressure and opening up clogged blood vessels, fewer people die of heart attacks and strokes. But we have to die of something—at least for the time being. So when one cause of death decreases, another must increase. Since it is easier to fix the body's pump and tubing system than to take control of rebellious cancer cells, more people die of cancer.

But cancer is not only about death and disease. It is also an important societal problem related to economics, ethics, and equality. One of the most problematic issues concerns who should receive what type of treatment. And even more important, who should be paying for it. In a wealthy country like Norway with a public health-care system, everybody generally receives the same level of service. When it comes to life-threatening conditions, people expect to get the best treatment that medical science can offer. The big problem is that this high level of care is not always possible to provide. As cancer research develops more advanced therapeutic methods, the treatment also becomes more expensive. Cancer therapies with impressive names like *personalized immunotherapy, stem cell transplantation*, or *intensity-modulated proton therapy* are far from cheap. Even the wealthiest countries in the world must therefore prioritize.

How much money should be used to save one human life when the same amount could be used to provide better health for hundreds of others? Should a heavy smoker with lung cancer receive the same level of health care as an elite athlete with leukemia? Is it worth spending hundreds of thousands of dollars to extend life for only a few more months—a life that may be filled with suffering? And what about the rich? Is it fair that affluent people can buy better treatment than everyone else?

These are complicated issues, and well-organized countries like Norway are trying to solve the problem by making a system for prioritizing patients and diseases. First, the effect of a new treatment must be documented by high-quality research, usually with a so-called *randomized controlled trial*, or RCT. Once a month, the directors of the health-care system then come together and decide which type of patients should receive which type of treatment. These decisions are based on three criteria determined by the government: How serious is the disease? How beneficial is the treatment? And how much does it cost?[4] Patients with a condition where the treatment is expensive and the effect is uncertain end up at the bottom of the list of priorities. Even if the research suggests that the patient may get some benefit from the medication, the leaders of the health-care system must make difficult decisions based on the predefined rules. Some treatments and diagnoses are rejected, and many patients get disappointed. Some may also have unrealistic expectations, and in the news, we read heartbreaking stories about patients in despair because they do not receive the latest and most expensive therapy.

People often say that you cannot put a price on the value of a human life. Still, we do it all the time. In the scientific field of health economics, the value of a life may be measured in *quality-adjusted life years* or QALYs. One QALY equals one year of perfect health, and for that, the statistic shows that Norway is willing to pay approximately 80,000 USD.[5] Since the life expectancy is about 80 years, we may multiply the two numbers and conclude that a newborn Norwegian is valued at 6,400,000 USD. That is about the same as the most expensive homes in Oslo. From that sum, we may then deduct 80,000 USD for each year you have lived and adjust a little up or down depending on your level of fitness. Thereby you get the price of your own life. A 95-year-old man with metastatic prostate cancer thus has very little left in his public health account, while a child with curable leukemia has a large endowment in the public health-care system.

To prioritize patients based on QALYs makes perfect sense in terms of socioeconomics but may seem brutal and unfair to those whose lives are depreciated. Still, this sense of injustice is nothing compared to how the health-care system works in many other countries. Most people in the world do not have a million-dollar public health account to charge when they get cancer. Obtaining personalized immunotherapy may be as realistic as going on a vacation to Mars. While people in privileged parts of the world can look back in horror at the times when malignant tumors were allowed to develop into large, painful monsters, this is still the reality for many. And the injustice is not limited to developing countries that lack resources and medical expertise. Often, it is simply a matter of the size of your bank account and whether you can afford health insurance or not. When some people argue about the availability of the newest experimental therapies, others cannot afford to pay for their child's most basic needs.

The point I am trying to convey is that the solution to cancer is not simply a matter of finding better ways to kill uncontrollable cells. It is also about money, equality, and the structures of society. In fact, if we take a slightly different perspective, cancer is not necessarily a problem at all. It can be seen as an enormous business opportunity. The global market for cancer therapy is estimated to be 135 billion dollars, and this number is expected to double by 2030.[6] What the general public may perceive as a lethal enemy, the biotech and pharmaceutical industry see as their most promising business segment. The meaning of cancer is thus always in the eye of the beholder.

A PERSONAL JOURNEY

Cancer may also be seen from a more personal perspective. While some patients are fighting an enemy, others describe the experience as a journey. It is a path with obstacles and uncertainty, often involving months and years of demanding treatment, leaving physical and mental scars. It may have its ups and downs, with family and friends as invaluable traveling companions. Finally, it is about facing death, not as a disappointing loss, but as a dignified end to a meaningful life—regardless of how long it lasted.

Though it may sound insensitive, despite its notorious reputation, cancer is not necessarily the worst way to die. On the contrary, dying of cancer is the best death, according to Richard Smith.[7] As the former editor of the *British Medical Journal* (*BMJ*), Smith is a highly respected voice in the medical community. And as may have been expected, his controversial statement garnered infuriated reactions.

Yet, Smith's line of argument seems both logical and well-formulated. He writes that, in principle, there are four different ways to die. One possibility is to die suddenly, for example, due to an accident or a heart attack. Many will probably say this is their preferred death, but Smith advises us to reconsider. What about your family and friends? Would it not be better to have time to prepare, plan the ending, and say a proper goodbye? In any case, if you are hoping for a quick death, you may want to ensure that all of your relationships and affairs are in order.

Another way is to die slowly from dementia. That implies that your memory and personality are gradually erased. In the end, only the body is alive. Death itself can be mild, but the years before are often difficult for the patient and even more so for the caretakers. The soul slowly disintegrates. And according to Smith, this may be the worst way to die.

The third option is to die of some form of organ failure, such as heart failure, kidney failure, or chronic pulmonary disease. These diseases can be a heavy burden over many years. Life is dominated by doctor visits, hospitalizations, and medication. Your quality of life is steadily declining, and death is unpredictable.

The last option is to die of cancer. And for most people, that is probably also the last choice. Cancer is associated with fear and pain, but according to Smith, dying of cancer is better than its reputation. Cancer death usually comes with a few years' notice or at least some months. You have time to prepare, but once it sets in, it is relatively quick, especially if you "stay away from overambitious oncologists."[8]

Smith describes cancer as a natural process where the physical and mental pains can be moderated with "love, morphine, and whiskey."[9] He admits that he is romanticizing, and most people will probably say that dying of cancer is anything but romantic. In general, we should be careful about ranking other people's experiences of illness and death. In the end, it is not necessarily the underlying diagnosis that matters.

Few people have described the journey of dying from cancer in more detail and depth than my former professor and later colleague, Per Fugelli. Building on his own experience, Per wrote about how death, especially from cancer, is taboo in our modern society. It is rarely talked about, and when it is, it is an evil we relentlessly strive to prevent.[10]

With his book *Døden, skal vi danse?* (*Death, Shall We Dance?*) Fugelli poetically aimed to "revive death."[11] He wanted to bring death out in the light, not as an enemy but as a partner, which sooner or later we all have to engage for a "dance." He described life with cancer as a journey of discovery, which was often troublesome and painstaking. Yet, it was also a great learning experience that brought meaning to life. "Cancer is not necessarily the Great Satan that must be fought by all means. Could cancer be a rose, albeit with thorns?" he asked provocatively.[12]

From my short career in clinical practice, I especially remember one patient. I was an intern in the medical department of a small hospital. And one of my patients was a 91-year-old man who had been hospitalized because of a sudden seizure. After a thorough examination and a range of tests, we found the probable cause. His entire chest was scattered with lymphomas. There was no prospect for a cure. He had probably only a few weeks to live, and it became my job to tell him the sad message.

Unlike today's medical students, I had not received much training on how to deliver such difficult information to vulnerable patients. Still, I did my best to be the kind of doctor I would have wanted to meet me in this situation. Fortunately, we ended up having a very nice conversation. The old man expressed that he was content and grateful for the life he had been given. The cancer was not really a threat, and he was ready to face death.

But the next day, the case took a dramatic turn. I received a phone call from the police. The message concerned my patient's 95-year-old wife, who had emptied a glass of sleeping pills and been found dead in her bed. The relatives had explained how she had given hints about her sad plans the day before. She could not live without her husband and insisted that *she* should be the first to leave.

So what is the right way to communicate this kind of message? I still do not know, but I sat by the old man's bed and told him what had happened. I listened to the little he had to say, and we held hands. My eyes got teary, and whether I was comforting him or he was comforting me was a bit blurry. My conduct was hardly professional, but right there and then, we made a heartfelt connection, and I got an important reminder that biomedicine sometimes has little to offer. Often empathy is the only and the best medicine there is.

AN ALTERNATIVE REALITY

Cancer may be approached from the perspective of biomedicine, the social sciences, and the humanities. But we should also be aware that many people have ideas about cancer that transcends all rational models of understanding. The world-famous, or infamous, Shaman Durek Verrett is a good example. As the fiancé of the Norwegian Princess Märtha and the friend of Hollywood star Gwyneth Paltrow, the self-declared spiritualist has received much attention for his alternative perspective on life and health, including some mind-boggling ideas about cancer. In the book *Spirit Hacking*, Verrett writes that he possesses supernatural powers that can "rotate" atomic nuclei and communicate with cells.[13] Thereby, he claims to be able to cure cancer, COVID-19, or any other disease.

Verrett also has an alternative explanation for the cause of cancer. He believes that tumors appear because the patient has negative thoughts, and he explains it like this: "When I go to hospitals, and I work with people who have cancer, the first question I always ask is: 'Why do you want this cancer?' That upsets some people. Kids, however, are not burdened by these kinds of hang-ups. When I work with children, and I ask them why they want their cancer, they tell me straight up: 'Because I don't want to be here anymore.'"[14]

While such alternative ideas raise few eyebrows in the erratic news cycles of Hollywood, they drew major headlines in Norway, not least because of Verrett's connection to the royal family. The massive criticism from the Norwegian Cancer Society and numerous medical experts forced the publisher to withdraw the book from the Norwegian market, and the most controversial passages were removed in the subsequent version. Yet, there is every reason to believe that Verrett actually means what he says and that he still preaches this alternative reality to his thousands of followers. As I am writing, you can buy Shaman Durek's "Spirit Optimizer" medallions for $222 apiece. They come in different colors, and the white version is said to "clear you from dark energy, fear-based thoughts, and negative emotions," while also being a remarkable cure for all variants of COVID-19.[15]

Verrett is, by no means, alone in explaining cancer and other diseases with a combination of magic and pseudoscience. An enormous market of individuals and companies offers various types of experimental cancer therapies based on dubious theories and weak evidence. They all claim to have the ultimate cure, and it is easy to get the impression that all cancers can be cured as long as you shop around and are willing to pay. The advertising can be convincing, and many desperate cancer patients spend everything they own, all of their strength and the limited time they have left, chasing a cure that never existed. Some may be lucky and experience an improvement, but there is often minimal evidence that it is related to the prescribed treatment. In far too many cases, the patient is left disappointed, exhausted, and poor. Or even worse, the patient is dead, while the grieving relatives are left with insurmountable debt.

There is no denying that many cancer patients have a positive attitude toward complementary medicine. Most shamans, healers, homeopaths, acupuncturists, kinesiologists, magnet therapists, and reflexologists are charismatic people who communicate compassion and sincerity. It is also easy to understand that patients in desperate situations are inclined to seek help wherever it is offered. To meet this demand, even reputable cancer clinics are offering complementary treatments or so-called integrative health services. They are thus balancing a fine line between being open-minded and supporting a movement that undermines rational thinking. Fancy theories about "strengthening the immune system," "stimulating paths of life-energy," and the homeopathic doctrine of "curing like with like" may sound convincing but have little or no support in actual science. That is why such treatments are *complementary*. If they had been documented by high-quality research, they would be actual medicine.

An abundance of research shows that the perceived effect of complementary medicine can be explained by the scientific principle commonly known as the placebo effect.[16] Placebo is medicine or treatment that we know does not work, typically a pill that contains no active substance whatsoever. But contrary to what many people believe, the placebo effect is not about deception or imagination.

Say that we are researching a new chemical substance that may improve the health of cancer patients. To test if it works, we give one group of patients pills containing the new medicine, while another group gets pills that look exactly the same but without the active ingredient. Neither the patients nor the doctors know who gets which type of pill until the experiment is over. To measure the effectiveness of the new treatment, we then calculate the difference between the group that got the chemical substance and those who got the placebo. That difference is the actual effect of the medicine.

The placebo effect, on the other hand, is the difference between the patients who got the placebo and a control group of similar patients who got no treatment at all. It is not the effect of the medicine, but the effect of everything else happening to the patients because of the research project. For example, the patients may have an increased level of activity since they are traveling to the hospital several times a month. Thereby, they also get important information about the disease. They may get the motivation to live healthier, or they may experience a desire not to disappoint the researcher.

The placebo effect is the effect of everything except the active substance. It does not kill malignant tumor cells, but it can significantly affect how we experience a disease. Having a sense of control can help patients cope with the most horrible condition, while fear and uncertainty can exacerbate a minute health issue into excruciating pain. We are consciously and unconsciously affected by what is happening physically and mentally, and getting medical treatment is a powerful situation. Medical treatment is not limited to the specific medication or surgical procedure. Even the color of the pills or the design of the packaging can affect whether patients experience improvement or not.[17] Body and soul are connected, and the whole situation affects us.

There is no question whether complementary medicine may positively affect a cancer patient's health. But it is not about supernatural abilities, magical pills, or pushing needles in fictional energy pathways.[18] It is about everything else that is going on in a patient's life. Providing support and understanding is good medicine no matter who gives it, and we should never underestimate the value of human care.

The biggest problem with complementary medicine is not that it does not work but that it distorts people's understanding of how the world and our bodies actually work. It is a shame that so many well-meaning therapists cannot help their patients without feeding them an elaborate skim of disinformation. Today, we pay much attention to fake news and why we should fight it. *Fake medicine,* however, has become an integrated and commonly accepted aspect of society. Critical voices are dismissed as arrogant and outdated. Many patients are therefore seduced, especially when the bogus theories are wrapped in a language of science. This effect has been particularly evident during the coronavirus pandemic. The active misinformation of the public has scared and manipulated people from being vaccinated, and there have been hundreds of thousands of unnecessary deaths.[19]

Scientific medicine has little effect if people do not have the knowledge and trust to take advantage of it. The fact that cancer patients try healing, acupuncture, or homeopathy may not be a big problem in each individual case. But overall, the massive misinformation of complementary medicine undermines people's ability to understand themselves and the world in general. Thereby it is also a threat to democracy.

AN ELEPHANT

Regardless of what some of us think of anti-vaxxers, complementary medicine, or Shaman Durek, we must accept that everybody has their own understanding of reality. The question of what cancer *is* may be answered in many different ways.[20] Where one researcher sees a technical challenge that can be solved with advanced bio-technology, another sees a societal problem related to prejudice and injustice. While some cancer patients experience their disease as a demanding but rewarding life journey, others are fighting for survival. A health politician sees enormous economic and social costs, while the CEO of a pharmaceutical company sees a lucrative market. Some see spirits and demons, while others are convinced that malignant tumors can be cured with herbs and diets. For some, the fight against cancer is a war that must be fought by all means For others, it is a conspiracy by doctors and researchers to ensure their own fame and fortune.

So who is right—what exactly is cancer? The ancient Indian parable of the blind men who meet their first elephant may help. They approach different parts of the animal and begin to describe, "Aha, this is a thick snake," says he who has a grip of the trunk. "No, it's a spear," yells the one holding a tusk. Another man has walked straight into the side of the large animal and is convinced that he has met a wall, while the one who got hold of the elephant's leg believes he is embracing a tree. "It's a fan," shouts the man holding on to one of the large ears, but he is quickly dismissed by the last one, who hangs on to the tail and says he got the end of a rope. They all give rational descriptions of the reality they observe, but no one understands much about the creature they have encountered.

Each of us sees only parts of reality. We collect fragments of information and connect them to what we already know. Thereby we create our own models of understanding. We make mental representations of the world we live in. How this mental model building takes place inside our brains is a fascinating problem. Think, for example, of how we as children learned the difference between an elephant and a giraffe. Today, we can tell the difference in a fraction of a second if somebody shows us a picture. We can interpret many different types of images, and we need to see only a small part of the animal to recognize it. That implies that we have somehow stored a complex and highly detailed model of both elephants and giraffes in our brains. Your model of an elephant and mine may not be exactly the same, but they probably combine all the observations of the six men in the previous story. In addition, they contain colors and movements, and if you have ever experienced an elephant up close, you also know how it smells. My first memory of an actual elephant comes from a traveling circus visiting my hometown in the 1970s, and the smell of an elephant is still strangely connected to the smell of popcorn.

Our ability to understand the world around us is based on the complex mental models that we build in our brains. The exact mechanisms by which these models are established and stored in the nervous system are still not fully understood, but recent research has shed new light on this fascinating topic. As a primary example, the Norwegian Nobel Prize winners May-Britt and Edvard Moser have conducted groundbreaking studies on how the brain maps our surroundings. They discovered a grid of brain cells that creates an interactive map where each cell corresponds to a specific position in the real world.[21] While some cells represent important landmarks, others mark the boundaries of the area, and still others register our direction and speed in the mental map.

This mental mapping is similar to how we see our GPS position moving in Google Maps as we move around. But our understanding of the world is not limited to a simple map. It is an intricate inner world filled with people, places, and everything we can imagine.[22] Our mental model is continuously refined and updated through the information we receive from our senses, allowing us to make complex decisions through advanced simulations carried out by the brain. In addition to our immediate surroundings, language and symbols give us the ability to construct mental models about things we have never experienced.

We even construct a model of ourselves.[23] As the most impor tant character in our own reality, this self-image serves as the center of all our mental world. Our personal avatar is the point of reference in everything we do and think, constructing our own unique identity. It represents who we are, to a much larger extent than our physical body does. And as we will come back to later, preserving our self-image, our consciousness, may be the ultimate solution to cancer.

The most advanced form of *virtual reality* is not a matter of mod ern computer technology. It exists inside our brains. We are separate individuals with separate identities, but our virtual worlds are also highly connected. You are now reading my thoughts. Language not only gives us the ability to make complex stories. It also allows us to share them in a highly effective manner. Mental models developed in one brain can be shared and further developed in others. Many mental models we have in common. Through generations, we have made laws and rules for how to interact and coexist, and together we have developed societies and cultures that are much more complex than any of us can comprehend on our own.

Together, we have also built increasingly more advanced models for how the world actually works. We have developed technology that enables us to communicate and explore aspects of life that oth erwise would be inaccessible to our ordinary senses. Using telescopes and space technology, we can create detailed maps of the universe and what it looks like on other planets. We use X-rays, magnetic fields, and biotechnology to explore the human body, right down to the smallest atom. And with the help of computer technology, we can analyze and simulate how all the different pieces fit together.

Our shared network of brains has gathered enormous amounts of information from various sources, and thereby we have built models of the world that are much more sophisticated and elaborate than what we could have developed on our own. I, for example, have never been to space, so I have never seen with my own eyes that the earth is shaped like a sphere and not flat as a pancake. A star in the sky looks to me like a dot of light. I have not been to the moon, and although the TV pictures seem convincing, I personally have no evidence that it is made of stone and not a big yellow cheese. Nor have I measured temperature changes in the atmosphere or studied the relationship between CO_2 emissions and climate change.

Nevertheless, I have a basic understanding of the solar system and the structure of the universe, and I believe that we have a climate crisis caused by a century of consumption of fossil fuels. So why is that? Why do I believe these descriptions of reality when I myself have never directly observed the phenomena? And what is it that separates my belief in the solar system, climate change, and medical science from people believing in healing, homeopathy, or supernatural powers?

These questions bring us to the center of the philosophy of science. The science of science is a complicated matter, but the most important lesson is that we should be careful about believing that we know anything at all. As Socrates said, "I know that I know nothing."[24] It is strictly impossible to know that something is completely true. There is always a possibility that if we examine the matter in a different way, from a different angle, or at a different time, it may look completely different. The best we can do is to explore the matter we want to understand in as many ways as possible. Then we check if these observations fit with our established model of reality. If it does not fit, we need to reevaluate the model. We check again, and if it still does not fit, we need to develop a new model. The more observations we make and the more information we gather, the better our model of reality will be. Understanding something is basically about seeing it from new perspectives, about the ability to ask new questions, and especially about the willingness to challenge our own beliefs.

That the earth is a sphere that orbits the sun, on the edge of a galaxy, in a universe that continues to expand after it was formed by a big bang is a theory that has been explored and tested in many different ways. Combined, this scientific model, based on decades of research, gives us a highly sophisticated understanding of the world we live in. Yet, thousands of researchers spend more or less their entire lives exploring and testing specific aspects of this model—because it can always be better. That is also true for our understanding of global warming. It is not the ultimate truth, but it explains an enormous number of scientific observations made with different methods, by different people in different places and at different times. Combined, it is the best explanation we have for what is currently happening to the climate.

At the opposite end of the scale, Shaman Durek's claim that he can cure disease by rotating atomic nuclei is a poor model. It does not fit with any of the other models, which, through generations of research, have been developed to explain the connection between cancer and atoms, and is only supported by his own assertions.

Although we can never say with one-hundred-percent certainty that the shaman cannot cure cancer by rotating atomic nuclei, such theories do little to help us understand how the world really works. It does not help to use scientific concepts when you do not recognize the scientific method and models that explain them. If Durek Verrett really wanted to understand cancer, he should have asked critical questions about his own extraordinary claims.

To understand elephants, global warming, or the universe, we must look at the issues from several different sides and put the observations together into a combined model. That is also how it is with cancer. Cancer is not a monster or cells that divide. It is not a societal problem or a lucrative market for the pharmaceutical industry. Nor is it a scientific problem or a punishment from God. The problem is that cancer can be all of this and more, all at the same time. Understanding cancer is not about learning a definition. It is about seeing the "elephant" from different angles. We must be able to switch from one point of view to another, see the different perspectives in combination, and then put them together in a larger construct. That is how science works, and it is also how we can develop our personal and common understanding of cancer.

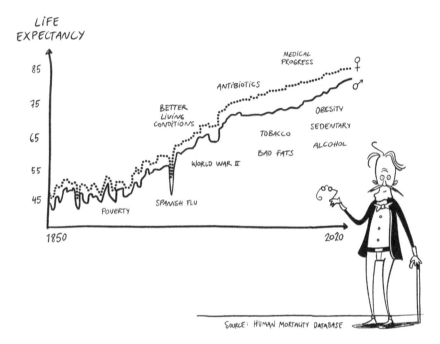

CHAPTER 5

The Cause

SMOKE WITHOUT FIRE

With a broadened understanding of what cancer *is*, we can take a step further and ask *why*. Why do we get cancer? Also this question can be answered in several different ways, but let us start with one of the most obvious.

We get cancer from smoking. "Smoking kills!" it says loud and clear on the label of cigarette packs, and it is estimated that one-third of all cancer cases are attributed to tobacco.[1] In addition, there are all the other diseases related to smoking, including coronary heart disease, stroke, diabetes, a number of lung diseases, birth defects, and much more. Smoking destroys health and ends lives. The easiest thing we can do to reduce the world's health problems is to quit smoking. But, unfortunately, that is easier said than done.

Cigarettes are intentionally designed to be addictive. The nicotine molecules in cigarette smoke act directly on the brain's reward system, which makes us want more of the same. The business model of the tobacco industry is to make their customers hooked on nicotine, making it physically and psychologically painful to quit. The fact that cigarettes kill approximately eight million people every year is of little concern to this ruthless industry. On the contrary, the tobacco companies have vigorously opposed every effort to inform and educate the public about the health risks of smoking, even though their own researchers confirmed the connection to cancer all the way back in the 1960s.[2]

Despite this cynicism, fierce political struggles and strict regulations have managed to restrain the sale and use of tobacco in most economically developed countries. Smoking on TV, on public transportation, or in restaurants is no longer acceptable, and there has been a promising decrease in the number of daily smokers in most OECD countries.[3] In Norway, only 1% of the population between the ages of 16 and 24 are daily smokers, and we can expect a significant reduction in lung cancer and other tobacco-related diseases in the coming decades.[4] Even more proactively, New Zealand recently proposed a law that will make it illegal to sell tobacco to people born in 2009 or later, aiming for the first smoke-free generation.

Globally, however, the situation is still gloomy. The tobacco industry has shifted its cynical strategy to new hunting grounds, to countries with lower levels of education, less regulation, and more corruption. Here, they can still manipulate the authorities and market cigarettes as an exciting and trendy product. They are explicitly targeting vulnerable teenagers who they can keep as nicotine slaves for the rest of their lives.[5] It is a terrible irony that the world spends enormous resources on health care and the development of new cancer drugs while the tobacco industry is actively producing new cancer patients.

Smoking undeniably leads to cancer, and you do not need to be a medical expert to predict that people will get sick from drawing thick tar smoke into their lungs several times a day. The knowledge that smoke and soot lead to cancer dates back to the 18th century, and similar to the tobacco industry, this case was also a matter of economic cynicism. This is the story of the impoverished boys in Victorian London who were sent half-naked to sweep the many factory chimneys that emerged during the Industrial Revolution. The boys lived miserable lives with malnutrition and poor hygiene and, not surprisingly, they developed numerous health issues. Quite extraordinarily, however, the young chimney sweepers developed a distinct form of cancer in the skin surrounding their testicles—not testicular cancer like Lance Armstrong—but *scrotal cancer.*[6]

The peculiar location of the cancers was related to the soot to which the boys were constantly exposed. The sticky substance accumulated in their underwear and got caught in the many wrinkles that are characteristic of the skin of the scrotum. The long-term exposure to soot then led to this unusual form of skin cancer, which grew further into the tissue and eventually turned into ugly infected tumors. Cases that were discovered early could be removed surgically, but since anesthesia had not yet been invented, it is easy to understand that many of the boys hesitated to seek help. Some even tried to cut out the tumors by themselves, but for many it had already gone too far. The cancer spread into the abdomen, and it is hard to imagine the pain and despair these already grossly exploited and humiliated boys had to endure.

The connection between chimney sweeping and cancer development was first described by the English physician Percivall Pott. His meticulous research is often cited as the first scientific documentation that cancer can be caused by environmental factors.[7] Such cancer-causing substances are generally referred to as *carcinogens*, and animal experiments have identified thousands of different chemicals that trigger and accelerate cancer development. Some are artificially produced in factories and laboratories, but many are entirely natural. Carcinogens are everywhere, at least in small doses, and the connection to smoke and soot is a recurring theme.

Since soot on the skin leads to skin cancer, and soot in the lungs leads to lung cancer, it almost goes without saying that soot in food leads to cancer of the intestines. Charcoaled food, like we get from barbequing meat or deep-frying potatoes, leads to the formation of several types of food carcinogens. People who consume such foods on a regular basis, therefore, have an increased risk of cancer, especially in the large intestines.[8]

Even Scandinavian crispbread, an epitome of health food, cannot be completely acquitted of cancer risk. This finding took the scientific community by surprise, and the unlikely path of discovery started in a leaky Swedish tunnel in the 1990s. To seal the leaks in the tunnel, the contractors decided to fill the cracks with a jelly substance known as acrylamide.[9] This chemical is a known carcinogen, and there were concerns about the health of the tunnel workers who were regularly exposed to the sticky substance. Researchers, therefore, took blood samples, and their worries were soon confirmed.

The tunnel workers had traces of acrylamides in their blood. For comparison, they then tested a control group of people who had not been working in the tunnel. The results were astonishing. They also had acrylamides in their blood. The control group was comprised of completely normal, crispbread-eating Swedes, and further research eventually discovered that the source was in the diet.

Before this study, acrylamide was primarily associated with the plastics and paper industry. As it turned out, however, the carcinogenic substance is also produced whenever foods containing carbohydrates are sufficiently heated. That includes the baking and frying of anything plant-based. In Sweden, crispbread and potato chips turned out to be the most important contributor to acrylamide in the food. It was a surprising finding, and although the cancer risk related to acrylamide is relatively low, health authorities have recommended that the food industry lower the cooking temperature for several food products.[10]

While we are on the topic of baking and cooking, we should also point out another important lesson from cancer research: Don't fry yourself. Excessive sunbathing, whether on the beach, in the high mountains, or in the solarium, causes skin cancer. The UV rays damage vital molecules inside the skin cells, and pale-skinned people are particularly vulnerable. Being white while longing for the sun is a bad combination, and that is why ethnic Northern Europeans are at the top of the statistics for all types of skin cancer.

People with fair skin get at least fifteen times more skin cancer than people with dark skin.[11] Accordingly, skin cancer is not just caused by sun exposure. It is also caused by the genes that determine a person's skin color. Skin cancer mainly occurs in those who have inherited the genes for light skin from their parents, while those with genes for dark skin are generally protected.

Usually, we focus on the fact that skin cancer is caused by sunlight. Therefore it is an environmental disease. At the same time, however, skin cancer is strongly related to skin color, which is highly hereditary. The relationship between sunlight, skin color, and cancer thus illustrates a crucial lesson: Cancer, or any other illness, is never caused solely by environmental or hereditary factors. It is always a combination of both.[12] The human body, and everything else living, is governed by genes that act in an environment, and neither have any meaning on their own. If we consider only people with light skin, we may conclude that skin cancer is due to environmental exposure to sunlight. Yet, their genetically determined skin color is the underlying reason why they are predisposed to the disease in the first place.

Similarly, a hereditary disease will always be affected by environmental factors. Take, for example, hereditary breast cancer. This congenital tendency to get cancer is linked to mutations in two specific genes referred to as the breast cancer genes, BRCA1 and BRCA2.[13] Women who have inherited certain variants of these genes from their parents have an increased risk of getting cancer. The risk is so high that some women choose to surgically remove their breasts instead of living in constant worry. But they still have an increased risk of getting cancer in other organs, and the best thing they can do is to delay the process by living as healthily as possible. Thereby they can delay cancer development for as long as possible. Genes and environment act in concert, and heritable breast cancer demonstrates why it is essential to see the two perspectives in combination.

The next time you hear that a disease is either environmental or hereditary, there is thus good reason to be critical.

The relationship between sunlight and skin color also illustrates another important concept. What exactly is the purpose of light skin? Why do not all people have dark skin to protect them from the sun's UV radiation? The point is that sunlight is also healthy. UV rays that penetrate the skin drive the chemical process that makes vitamin D, which, as the name implies, is vital to our health. The farther away we get from the equator, the less sun there is, and the lighter skin people need to let the sun's rays into their cells. Through evolution, inhabitants of the northern regions have therefore developed less pigmentation than those in the south.[14] Dark-skinned immigrants, on the other hand, may get too little sunlight and should be extra careful to get enough vitamin D by eating fish or taking supplements.

The cause of cancer is often a complex balance between many different factors. Too much, as well as too little, can be a problem. The connection between cancer and estrogen is an illustrative example. Estrogen, the primary female sex hormone, is produced in the ovaries and affects many different processes in the body. Among other bodily functions, it regulates the menstrual cycle, which is precisely why there is estrogen in birth control pills.

Estrogen is one of many signal molecules that regulates cell division. Thereby it also affects cancer development, but the relationship is far from simple.[15] Research shows that estrogen both increases and decreases the risk of cancer. While the hormone increases the risk of developing cancer in the breasts and the cervix, it has a protective effect on cancer of the uterus, ovaries, and colon.

The long-term effect of estrogen on the cells in the body is related to several different factors. Having late puberty, multiple pregnancies, and early menopause generally implies less exposure to estrogen, while taking birth control pills or estrogen supplements after menopause work in the opposite direction. All these factors thereby affect the level of estrogen in the body. Estrogen then affects cell division, which in turn affects cancer development. Whether this effect is positive or negative then depends on the molecular mechanism inside the cells of the different organs. The body is a complex system, and estrogen clearly illustrates how complicated it can be to define the causes of cancer. Inheritance and environment, lifestyle and life cycle, and internal and external factors play together in an intricate network.

Some cancers are also related to virus infections. Cervical cancer, for example, is not just influenced by estrogen. It is even more strongly related to the virus that causes common warts, the human papillomavirus, or HPV.[16] This virus is typically spread through sex, and cervical cancer is arguably also a sexually transmitted disease— an STD. That is why sexually abstinent nuns rarely get this type of cancer. Importantly, however, it is not the cancer cells that are contagious but the virus that has infected them. HPV enters the cells and overrides their control system to make copies of itself, thereby increasing the chance that the cells run wild.

The positive aspect is that HPV infection, like most other virus infections, can be prevented by vaccination. Today, boys and girls all over the world are immunized against HPV. When they grow up, both men and women are thus immune to the sexually transmitted virus, and recent research shows that these vaccination programs dramatically reduce the incidence of HPV-related cancers.[17]

Another virus that contributes to cancer development is the Epstein-Barr virus. EBV is best known for causing mononucleosis or kissing disease, but this infection also increases the risk of developing a particular form of cancer. So-called Hodgkin's lymphoma typically affects people between the ages of 20 and 40, and genetic analyses show that EBV is involved in approximately half of the cases.[18]

Virus-related cancers are especially prevalent among people with a weakened immune system, and sometimes different viruses seem to team up against us. The human immunodeficiency virus, HIV, does not cause cancer on its own. Instead, it hijacks the body's defense and opens the door for other viruses. That leads to a wide range of other infectious diseases, and the patient develops a condition known as AIDS—acquired immune deficiency syndrome.

As the immune system is weakened, the body is also more vulnerable to the viruses that contribute to cancer development. One type of cancer is found almost exclusively among AIDS patients. So-called Kaposi's sarcomas are caused by particular strains of the herpes virus.[19] The tumors can occur anywhere in the body but are typically observed as purple spots on the skin. This ominous sign of disease was a common sight in the 1990s, at the peak of the HIV pandemic. Today, however, AIDS is a rare condition due to new antiviral medication that stops the virus from replicating inside our cells. There is also a lot of research aiming to develop an HIV vaccine. But because the virus attacks the cells that generate the immune response, this task has proven excruciatingly difficult.

Once again, it is important to emphasize that cancer is not contagious in itself. We do not get cancer from being near, hugging, or even having sex with a cancer patient. It is practically impossible to get infected with somebody else's cancer. Yet, there are some very rare and interesting exceptions.

The most exotic example concerns the Tasmanian devil, an aggressive marsupial that lives on the isolated island state of Tasmania in southeast Australia. These animals tend to develop a peculiar kind of cancer, most commonly in the facial region. Unlike ordinary cancers, these malignant tumors have not developed from the animal's own cells. Instead, the cancer cells are transmitted as the "devils" fight and bite each other. Cancer cells from one individual thereby infect the wounds of another. There, the malignant cells continue to grow and infiltrate the new host. Cancer cells that arose in a Tasmanian devil several decades ago have thus spread throughout the population. At one point, the disease even threatened to eradicate the entire species. But today, breeding programs for healthy animals are helping the situation.

Scientists have shown that there are two different strains of cancer cells that spread among the Tasmanian devils, one that originated in a female and one that originated in a male.[20] The unique thing about these cancer cells is that they are not detected and eliminated by the animals' immune systems. In humans and most other species, cells from one organism will be rejected by the body of another. That is why it is so hard to transplant organs from one person to another, and that is also true for cancer cells. The cancer cells of the Tasmanian devils, however, have found a way to avoid the immune system, not only of its original host but also the immune system of the entire population. Researchers are therefore investigating the Tasmanian devil to better understand the relationship between cancer and the immune system.

That brings us to another extraordinary way of getting cancer: organ transplantation. When transplanting kidneys or other organs from one human to another, there is always a small possibility that the transplanted organ contains cancer cells, which neither the donor nor the doctors had detected.[21] As transplantation has become increasingly more common and organs are obtained from increasingly older donors, such unintentional transplantation of cancer has become a serious problem.

If cells from other people enter our bodies, they are normally detected and eliminated by the immune system. That is why patients with transplanted organs must always take drugs that inhibit this immunologic reaction. Otherwise, the transplanted organ will be rejected and die. Patients who have received an organ containing cancer cells, therefore, represent a difficult dilemma: Should the immune system be allowed to do its job and kill the cancer, thereby risking the transplanted organ? Or should it be suppressed, thereby allowing the cancer to spread?

Cancer treatment involves many dilemmas, and one of the most difficult is that the treatment itself can be a cause of cancer. The discovery of radiation therapy for young lymphoma patients is one of the great successes in the history of medicine. As the patients grew older, however, many developed new, so-called secondary cancers in the irradiated region of the body. Young women who received radiation therapy for lymphomas in the chest often developed breast cancer and heart problems later in life.[22]

It may seem illogical to use something that gives cancer to cure cancer, but in this context, the war metaphor can be quite useful. The purpose of chemo and radiation therapy is to kill cancer cells, and in the heat of battle, it is almost impossible not to damage the normal cells in the body. Thus collateral damage causes both short- and long-term side effects. Even though cancer treatment has become more targeted and the doses of radiation and chemotherapy have been optimized, the cost of survival is often high.

Especially for young patients, cancer treatment is a double-edged sword. They have a long life ahead of them, and severe late effects may develop decades after they are declared cured and cancer-free. Finding the balance between lifesaving treatment and potentially debilitating late effects is difficult. And the risk of secondary cancers is only a part of the problem. Other late effects involve fatigue, heart disease, impaired sexual function, difficulty sleeping, learning disabilities, and several other conditions. For many patients, being a cancer survivor is a chronic condition that may represent a severe reduction in quality of life. Health professionals must therefore be aware and honest about these challenges. All cancer patients should be well-informed and actively involved in the decision-making process concerning their own treatment.

The issue of possible late effects is easy to push aside when a patient is finally cured. It is time to go on, and both the doctors and the patients may want to focus on the positive. Yet, omitting the prospect of late effects may have severe and sometimes deadly consequences. Cancer survivors need knowledge and support to take extra care of their physical and mental health—to adjust their diet, stay fit, and go for regular checkups. The difficult message about late effects should not be swept under the carpet.[23]

CANCER FROM LIVING

The causes of cancer are numerous and complicated, and so far, we have only discussed a few illustrative but important examples. We can get cancer from heavy metals in seafood, pesticides on fruits and vegetables, mold in the walls of our houses, chemicals in cosmetics, and exhaust from car traffic. There is asbestos in old buildings, microplastics in the sea, and chlorine in the drinking water. Other cancer-causing factors include radon gas that seeps up from the ground or radioactive fallout deposited in the soil around the world from the nuclear accident in Chernobyl in 1986. From there, the radioactive isotopes make their way to the food chain and our dinner table.

We also get cancer from eating entirely normal food, especially if we eat so much that it leads to obesity.[24] Due to sedentary work and free access to fat and sugar in all varieties, the population is getting increasingly overweight. After smoking, obesity is the most important risk factor for cancer. The association is clear, but the causal relationship is complicated. Obesity affects many biochemical processes in the body, but somewhat simplified, it appears that the excess energy makes our cells run a bit faster. Thereby they also get more prone to going astray and turning into cancer.

The list of causes and risk factors for cancer is almost inexhaustible, and it is important to distinguish between those that really matter and those that are just good to know. What may seem most frightening, like radioactivity and toxic waste, is not necessarily what should concern us the most.

For example, there has been much attention related to cancer and electromagnetic radiation from high-voltage power lines, radio transmitters, fuse boxes, and mobile phones. Many have been concerned, and much research has been done to clarify the issue. And the results are clear: To the extent that ordinary electromagnetic fields cause cancer, the risk is minute relative to all the other factors.[25]

The main causes of cancer are generally the most common and boring. To avoid cancer, we should first of all focus on our own lifestyle. The most important advice is very well-known and exceedingly dull: Stop smoking. Eat more vegetables, less meat, and fewer sweets. Drink less alcohol and sugar soda, be active, and use sunscreen. It is that easy and still so difficult. All the other factors are not without significance, but unless you have a particular working environment or a special life situation, there is good reason to focus on the most common and well-documented causes of cancer.

Say that you are sitting in your garden enjoying the bright sun after a delicious barbecue steak and a large glass of red wine. According to the scientific evidence, the electromagnetic radiation from the nearby power line should be the least of your concerns. My point is not to spoil the joys of life, but it is important to see the different risks and causes in perspective.

We seem to get cancer from almost everything—especially the things that, for many, make life worth living. And that is exactly the point. We get cancer from living. The most important risk factor for getting cancer is neither genetics nor environment. It is age. While getting cancer in childhood and adolescence is a terrible tragedy, it is fortunately quite rare. Fewer than 1% of cancer patients are under the age of 20. The vast majority are well above 50 years old, but from that age the curve rises sharply.[26] The "harder" we live and the older we get, the greater the chance of getting cancer.

Systematic analysis of dead bodies, so-called autopsy studies, show that cancer development is strongly related to aging. Prostate cancer, the most common cancer among men, is a good example. For men above 50, the percentage with early stages of prostate cancer is approximately the same as their age. Cancer cells are found in almost 50% of 50-year-olds, while the proportion rises to as much as 90% in 90-year-olds.[27] Most men die *with* and not *from* the disease, but the trend is clear. Prostate cancer increases with age, and most other types of cancer show a similar pattern. If you get old enough, you are almost guaranteed to have cancer somewhere in your body. A centenarian who has not been diagnosed with some form of cancer has just not been thoroughly examined—and it is probably best to leave it like that.

Aging is also the main reason there are increasingly more people with cancer in the world: People generally live longer than before. Except for two significant downward peaks during the Spanish flu and the World Wars, life expectancy has risen steadily since 1900.[28] This remarkable development is related to improvements in working and living conditions, better diet, and health care that offers vaccines, antibiotics, and regular checkups. Young people no longer die of measles or tuberculosis. Modern medicine opens up clogged blood vessels and replaces damaged heart valves. In many countries, life expectancy has increased by as much as ten years since the 1950s. While reaching the age of a hundred used to be a sensation, there are now over half a million centenarians in the world.[29] Of today's babies, maybe as many as one-third will live to be a hundred in some countries.

Cancer development is strongly related to aging, and the current cancer epidemic is actually a great success story. It is the story of how our quality and length of life have steadily increased due to societal and technological developments. Better living conditions and modern medicine have saved many lives, and for every life saved, the average age of the population has increased. As the population grows older, we get more cancer.

This relationship between cancer and aging thus involves a formidable paradox: The better we become at treating cancer and other diseases, the longer we live and the more cancer there will be in the population. Modern medicine is not solving the problem of cancer. On the contrary, medical and technological developments are the cause of the growing cancer epidemic. Our own striving to live as long as possible produces more cancer.

This paradox becomes even more difficult when we consider that cancer is also a hereditary disease. Testicular carcinoma, the type of cancer that affects young men, is a good example. A few decades ago, this disease was highly lethal, and less than half of the patients survived. Today, almost all are cured, and many of the patients live on to have children. Studies of these children show that the boys have four times higher risk of testicular cancer than their peers.[30] The tendency to get testicular cancer is inherited, and since the patients now live on to have children, there will be more of this cancer in the population.

So, what can we do? Should we end medical research and stop treating people with cancer? Should we set an upper limit for how long people are allowed to live, or should only healthy people be allowed to have children? That sounds like a terrible tyranny, and it is hardly the type of society any of us are hoping for. In theory, we can go back to the way it was before. In the Middle Ages, few people lived long enough to get cancer. One may wonder if that made them more or less happy than people of today, but most of us are probably pleased to avoid sword fighting and famine or the fear of dying from a simple bacterial infection.

We all want to live as long as possible, at least as long as we are reasonably healthy, and it seems utterly inconceivable that we as a society should choose to live shorter than we do today. We may experience setbacks. In the United States, the opioid crisis and the growing social inequality have led to a recent decline in overall life expectancy.[31] Yet the rich are still getting older, and the long-term trend seems clear.

There is also the possibility that a nuclear war or a meteor disaster may take us back to the Middle Ages or even eradicate our species. For the time being, however, we should expect that the trend toward higher life expectancy and more cancer will continue. If we are going to cure cancer "once and for all," as President Obama promised, we must do something much more radical than just keep on killing cancer cells. It will require a fundamental transformation of our own existence.

FADING FLOWERS

"To be or not to be," said William Shakespeare's Prince Hamlet as he struggled to find the meaning of life.[32] So why do we live? While some find answers in religion and spirituality, others see meaning in the concrete, like spending time with family and friends, experiencing the wonders of nature, or creating something new. If we take a scientific perspective, however, the meaning of life is basically all about sex. The immediate reason you and I exist is that our parents, our grandparents, and all of our ancestors had successful intercourse. Not necessarily successful in the sense that it was a good experience. For many, it was perhaps anything but memorable. We are talking about success in the sense that it led to conception and eventually to the birth of a viable child.

Throughout history, there have been millions of people who did not have children. Many died of disease or injury even before puberty. Some may have been interested in neither children nor family, while others had mental, social, or financial problems that made it difficult to find a partner. Some had disabilities that prevented intercourse. There were women with clogged fallopian tubes and men with sperm that could not swim. Some had multiple miscarriages, while others had babies with lethal birth defects. They tried and tried but still did not succeed.

A lot has changed through the ages, but the general principle still applies: Far from everyone has children. In many economically and technologically developed countries, more people live their lives childless than ever before. The reasons are biological, as well as cultural. Women especially are at their most fertile in their twenties. Then fertility gradually declines until ending at menopause. As women of today wait longer than previous generations to have children, the chance of them not getting pregnant has increased.

Similarly, an increasing proportion of the male population never has children. This development has been related to declining sperm quality, but the most important reason is that many of today's women have children with a relatively smaller fraction of men.[33] These men, who for some reason are more successful at attracting a mate, thus have children with two or more women, while other men wander childlessly through life. The phenomenon, generally referred to as being *involuntary celibate* or an *incel* for short, has become a central issue in modern culture. Incels are usually men, and they are portrayed by themselves and others as misogynistic and aggressive. They hate women and society for being deprived of sex and love.[34]

Sex is an important aspect of society, psychologically and culturally, but more than anything, it determines our biological evolution. We may not think about it in everyday life, but sex and procreation always involve an aspect of selection. Physical strength and natural beauty may not be as important as before, but good health, intelligence, and social skills still affect our ability to conceive and raise children. This decision of who shall pass on their traits to the next generation is a complex process with fundamental consequences.

Considering all the obstacles, it is quite amazing that there are so many of us. It is an astonishing yet obvious fact that absolutely all of our ancestors found a sexual partner with whom they had at least one child. This child then grew up and did exactly the same, and so it continued. The line goes all the way back to the evolution of the human species, *Homo sapiens*, on the savannas of Africa more than 300,000 years ago. From there, it continues to our apelike ancestors, through rodents, reptiles, amphibians, and fish, and all the way to the first cell that formed the basis of life on earth. We, the people of today, are all the result of a four-billion-yearlong, completely uninterrupted success story.

Life on earth started as a small cell. That is also how yours and my life began the day we were conceived in our mother's womb. A human life begins when a sperm cell, developed in one of the man's testicles, swims through the woman's uterus and into one of her two fallopian tubes. If it is lucky, it encounters an ovum slowly moving in the opposite direction, on its way from the corresponding ovary. Then the two cells merge to form a fertilized egg cell, also known as a zygote. This cell then divides again and again until it becomes a small embryo that attaches to the inside of the uterus. There it grows and develops, and after approximately nine months, a child is born.

That is how it has always been and how we will always continue to make children. Or maybe not. On the 25th of July 1978, something exceptional happened in the history of the human species. Louise Joy Brown was born at a hospital in England.[35] No, it is not the story of a divine prophet conceived by a holy spirit. But it is as close as you can get with the help of modern biotechnology. Louise was the world's first test-tube baby—the first human being not to be conceived in her mother's womb as a result of sexual intercourse. She was made in a laboratory.

With the invention of test-tube babies, or in vitro fertilization, it is no longer necessary to find a partner of the opposite sex to have children.[36] Today, egg and sperm cells can be ordered online. There are sperm and egg banks all over the world, and based on detailed information about the donors including their genetic characteristics, you may pick your own combination.

Different countries have different laws and procedures, but for those with money and connections, there is a wide range of opportunities. You may design a child with the right gender, skin color, and level of intelligence. Perhaps most importantly, you can eliminate a range of genetic diseases. The embryo can then be inserted into a uterus for hire. The owner of this uterus is generally referred to as a surrogate mother, even though she is neither the biological mother nor will she be the sociological mother of the child. This way, you may have a child without having either sex or being pregnant. It may be derived from your own genetic material, or it may not. The result may not turn out exactly the way you expect, but in principle, you can design your own child.[37]

Sperm and egg donation, in vitro fertilization, fetal diagnostics, and surrogate mothers have become a part of the common vernacular. Children are made systematically in laboratories instead of the complicated and unpredictable method of sexual intercourse. Germ cells and embryos are frozen in liquid nitrogen in large clinics, and human seedlings have become a commercial product. Most people may take little notice, but we are in the middle of a biological, technological, and cultural revolution with unforeseeable implications. For millions of years or even hundreds of millions of years, children were made on the basis of their parents' ability to find a partner, have sexual intercourse, and carry a viable fetus. Today, all these barriers have been lifted. It is also only a matter of time before we have artificial uteruses. Thereby we will circumvent the problematic issue of surrogate mothers, and the whole process of producing children can be carried out in a laboratory. That may sound like speculative science fiction, but we have already taken the most significant steps toward a world where the production of humans, from cell to full-born child, can be carried out like an industrial process.

How this development is related to cancer will become clear in a moment. First, we need to understand the normal cells of the human body. Where do they come from, and how do they work? So let us start at the beginning, with the zygote. With a diameter of 0.1 millimeter, it is right at the threshold of what is possible to see with the naked eye. Yet, it contains the whole recipe for a new and unique human being.

An intriguing question thus arises: If the zygote can become a human being, does it also qualify as a person? This fundamental question lies at the heart of the ferocious debate for or against abortion. When does a lump of cells become an individual with moral and legal rights in society? That is not an easy question to answer. Embryonic development involves a gradual transformation from a single cell to a viable human being. There is no easily definable point or threshold where it transcends from one to the other. As for many other things in life, it depends on our perspective, and different societies have come to different conclusions. In many countries, the general limit for abortion is the 12th week of pregnancy.[38] Then the fetus is about six centimeters from head to bottom. It weighs about eighteen grams, with tiny fingers, toes, and all the other characteristics of a minute human being.

Hard-line opponents of abortion will argue that there is no limit at all. They believe that life begins at conception. The zygote is equal to a human being, and abortion is, by definition, murder. Maybe they are correct, but let us do a little thought experiment to explore the problem.[39] Say there is a fire in your local fertility clinic. You are the first responder, and while standing in an inferno of smoke and flames, you must make a difficult decision. Are you going to save the elderly receptionist lying unconscious on the floor, or will you carry out the nitrogen tank with a thousand frozen embryos standing next to her? For the sake of argument, let us say that they are of similar weight and just as difficult to carry.

Most people would probably, without hesitation, choose the actual person on the floor. Even if, in theory, we can save a thousand lives by choosing the tank of embryos, our intuition and conscience tell us something else. Even though it is difficult to pinpoint, something fundamental happens during the first weeks of pregnancy. To most people, there is a significant difference between a cell, which may become a human being, and an actual person.

The transformation from a single cell to a multicellular organism is one of the most amazing wonders of life, and there is still a lot to understand. In principle, however, we have a general understanding of how it happens.[40] Approximately one day after fertilization, the zygote divides and forms two copies of itself. These two cells then divide again, and so it continues. After a few days, the collection of cells looks like a small mulberry—called a *morula* in Latin. If everything goes according to plan, this "berry" attaches itself to the inside of the uterus. Then the magic begins. The cells continue to divide, but they are no longer exactly alike. Instead, they develop into three different layers of cells with different properties, generally referred to as the germ layers. The inner germ layer, called the *endoderm*, rolls up to form a tube that extends from the mouth to the buttocks. These cells give rise to the entire digestive system, including the esophagus, the stomach, and the small and large intestines. The tube also branches off to form the liver, pancreas, trachea, and lungs. The middle germ layer, the *mesoderm*, becomes everything that has to do with the blood, including the red and white blood cells, all the blood vessels, the spleen, the kidneys, the lymph nodes, and the heart. All the muscles and the skeleton also come from this middle layer of cells. Finally, we have the outer germ layer, the *ectoderm*, which forms the wrapping. It becomes the skin, the nails, all the hair, and the tooth enamel. Additionally, a part of the ectoderm bulges into the middle layer and becomes the brain, the spinal cord, and the entire nervous system.

The cells in the three germ layers develop in different directions.[41] They differentiate into a range of specialized cell types and bind together in three-dimensional networks that form our various organs. Some types of cells, such as nerve cells, lie more or less still and do their job throughout life. Others, like skin cells, blood cells, and the cells covering the inside of the intestines die after a few days and are replaced by new ones. While old and worn-out cells die, the so-called *stem cells* continue to divide.

Once again, we may draw a comparison to an ant colony. Or, more precisely, our body is a collection of several colonies working together. The zygote gives rise to different types of stem cells that are constantly renewing the different organs. The blood stem cells keep making all the different blood cells. The cells that make up the gut's mucous membrane are continuously renewed by stem cells in small glands all along the intestines, while stem cells at the bottom of the outer skin layer make new skin cells.

Our body is not a machine. It is a complex society of cells where the organs represent communities with dedicated functions. The different cell types may be seen as specialized trades or professions with different roles and functions in the cellular society. They are all descendants of the zygote, and after nine months of cell division and development, a baby is born. Then begins what we call *life*, although the most complicated and astonishing part of the process is already completed.

How long this life will last, nobody knows. The only thing that is certain is that we will gradually get older, get cancer or other diseases, and eventually die. So what is the point? What is the meaning of it all? I am not referring to the *meaning of life* in the religious or philosophical sense. That is something each of us must figure out for ourselves. I am still regarding the world from a biological perspective, and the question should be interpreted in the literal sense: Why does the zygote divide and develop in different directions? Why do these cells form a brain, a heart, and all the other organs? And ultimately, what is the purpose of making a human body, which sooner or later will collapse and die due to cancer and aging?

The answer lies in the early stages of embryonic development—in an event that happens within the first week of conception.[42] It involves the formation of a group of cells, which are neither part of the inner germ layer, the middle germ layer, nor the outer germ layer of the body. Instead, they originate from the *yolk sac*—a bulge on the embryo corresponding to the egg yolk of an ordinary breakfast egg. These are the *germ cells*, which eventually will develop into new sperm and ova.

Notice that this terminology may be somewhat confusing. Notice that the germ layers, which give rise to all the cells of the body and the germ cells, which give rise to sperm and ova, are two different things.

The germ cells do not really belong to the body and have their own path through life. From their origin in the yolk sac, they crawl and swim through the emerging umbilical cord and into the tiny body. There they enter the organs that later in life will become either ovaries or testicles. Then they wait until they get the signal to develop into either sperm or ova. And then they wait a bit more. They are waiting for sex.

The life mission of the germ cells is to make their way to the next uterus, and they start preparing for their big leap even before they have left the previous one. Before we are born, the germ cells find their place in the ovaries and testicles, and there they wait for the big escape. Sex is their only chance to survive. At least, that is how it was until the invention of in vitro fertilization.

So, now we are approaching the meaning of it all: The germ cells, which crawled into the body during the first weeks of development, are the only cells that will go on to the next generation. All the other cells—the cells that form our actual body—find themselves at an evolutionary dead end. They are workers and soldier ants that will keep on working and fighting until they die. Thereby, they ensure that the germ cells—representing the queen—will fly away to make a new colony.

The human body is not designed to live as long as possible. Its purpose is to pass on the germ cells to the next generation. The meaning is to procreate. We must produce children, and then we must raise them. Human offspring must be fed, dressed, and protected from dangers. They must learn to speak and obtain knowledge and skills to help them cope in a highly challenging environment. While many species leave their eggs or the live-born offspring to fend for themselves, children are entirely dependent on their dedicated caregivers. The passage of the germ cells depends on parents living long enough to raise their children so they can manage on their own.

Grandparents may also be highly valuable.[43] They provide support for both children and grandchildren. At some point, however, there is a limit. Having eight surviving great-grandparents or sixteen great-great-grandparents is not necessarily an advantage. On the contrary, they also need food, care, and housing. They will consume valuable time and energy, thus hampering the germ cells' passage through the generations.

It may sound cynical, but as we get older, it is actually beneficial to our descendants that we die. In fact, it is an absolute necessity. If nobody dies, there would simply not be enough space and resources to raise new children. The only solution would be to find another inhabitable planet, and even that would be full within a few years.

In this perspective, there is a simple logic to the fact that cancer and many other diseases increase dramatically from the age of 70. In the same way that various cells commit suicide when they are no longer needed, our body is programmed to disintegrate and shut down when it has completed its biological purpose. This scientific model is often referred to as the disposable body theory.[44] It is based on the basic principle of evolution, and as we will discuss later, it can explain many processes related to aging and cancer development.

The body may be seen as a beautiful flower that ensures the germ cells' passage through the generations. When the seeds are fertilized and lie safe and ready in the soil, the organism has fulfilled its purpose. Sooner or later, autumn comes. We wither and die—while life goes on.

A AND B MOLECULES
FLOATING AROUD

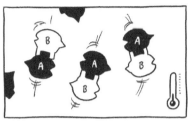

FORMING PAIRS
AT LOW TEMPERATURE

MAY ALSO CONNECT IN CHAINS

A CHAIN CONNECTS FREE MOLECULES
AND MAKE A NEW ONE

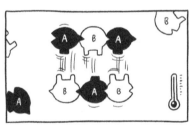

THE TWO CHAINS DISSCONNECT
AT HIGH TEMPERATURE

TWO CHAINS BECOME FOUR,
FOUR BECOME EIGHT...

ERRORS IN REPLICATION
LEADS TO MUTATIONS

DIFFERENT MUTANTS COMPETE
FOR MOLECULES

CHAPTER 6

The Principle

DARWIN'S IDEA

The fact that cancer increases with age is a result of how our body is constructed. But that is not a good choice of words. It was not actually constructed. The body has evolved. If we want to understand cancer, we thus need to understand Charles Darwin's famous theory of evolution. So, what was it that Darwin discovered as he circumvented the world on the HMS *Beagle* while exploring all kinds of plants and animals? As before, there is no simple answer and many misunderstandings.

Darwin's groundbreaking book *The Origin of Species* is an approximately 500-page scientific study of life on earth and how it has evolved.[1] It is a story about how plants and animals live, reproduce, and die. It also describes how fossils of different species are layered in the earth according to their age. First and foremost, it describes a simple scientific theory that explains all these observations. Darwin argued that life has evolved over millions of years, and the most controversial part was the idea that "humans descended from apes." Or, to be more precise, humans, chimpanzees, and all other animals have a common origin. One may just as well say that we descended from fish or amoebae.

Darwin's theory of evolution explains how all the different species are related. But contrary to popular belief, the main point was not that life has evolved from something simpler. Scientists and philosophers had proposed that idea many years before Darwin. The French biologist Jean-Baptiste Lamarck is well known for his theory that species evolve because the offspring inherit traits the parents acquired during their lives.[2] This theory implies that a couple of bodybuilders should get children with larger muscles than if the parents had not lifted weights. A mother who wears tight shoes should have children with small feet, and a father who sunbathes a lot should have offspring with darker skin. Today, we know that this is not how heredity and evolution work. As discussed in the previous chapter, only the germ cells are passed on to the next generation. Children do not inherit changes that occur in the other cells of their parents' bodies—at least not through genetic inheritance.

Children may indeed inherit both habits and skills that their parents have acquired. As one of many examples, parents who smoke cigarettes more often get children who also smoke cigarettes. But such social inheritance is transmitted by thoughts, not genes. These are two completely different modes of inheritance involving different types of information, but as we will come back to later, there is a fundamental connection. There are also other mechanisms by which the parents' lives can affect the offspring. The mother's diet, alcohol use, and age may significantly impact embryologic development. Such *epigenetic* changes are also related to the theory of evolution, but that requires a longer explanation, which we will also return to later.

First, we need to resolve another widespread misunderstanding about Darwin's fundamental discovery. Throughout history, many people, including medical doctors, biologists, and other scientists, have wrongfully concluded that the theory of evolution says something about who should live and who should die. Darwin spoke of *survival of the fittest*. And many have interpreted this phrase to mean that people who are strong and healthy are more worthy of living than those who are somehow weak or sick. The theory of evolution is often confused with concepts like *the law of the jungle* or *the right of the strongest*, implying that individuals somehow deemed inferior do not have the right to live.

This idea that deviant individuals should be eliminated, or at least be prevented from reproducing, is generally referred to as *eugenics*.[3] It can be traced back to ancient philosophers like Plato and is probably as old as human civilization. This way of thinking was also well established in the class society of Victorian England and was quickly related to the theory of evolution. In the wake of Darwin's work, an ideology emerged in which the ranking and selection of human beings were legitimized by seemingly scientific arguments, often with reference to the theory of evolution. The term *eugenics* was introduced by Darwin's half cousin Francis Galton as part of a general ideology commonly known as social Darwinism.[4]

The basic reasoning was that a society that helps the weak and the sick works opposite to natural selection. Unless we actively eliminate these "inferior qualities," we are therefore in danger of driving humanity toward damnation or at least toward mediocrity. From this line of argument, it was further concluded that the social elite, and especially the medical profession, had a moral obligation to eliminate bad traits from the population.

At the beginning of the twentieth century, many countries had laws and procedures to execute this logic. For example, the purpose of the Norwegian Sterilization Act of 1934 was "increased control of inferior individuals' reproduction of the species."[5] The term "inferior" alluded primarily to people with mental illness or developmental disabilities, but ethnic minorities and other "deviants" were also forcibly sterilized. Some were sterilized while still children, without understanding why or what the procedure entailed. Today forced sterilization is seen as a human rights violation, and most democratic countries reject the idea and practices of eugenics. More authoritarian regimes, however, are still using sterilization as a means of control and oppression. Most notably, China is internationally condemned for atrocities, including forced sterilization, against the country's Uyghur minority.[6]

While eugenics and racial theories are a common theme throughout human history, the Nazi ideology developed these ideas to the extreme. Based on pseudoscientific theories, they ranked people with different ethnicities, anatomical characteristics, sexual orientations, and diseases in a hierarchy of superhumans and underhumans. Skin color was especially defined as a token of human value, and the light-skinned Germanic and Aryan races were obviously situated at the top of the pyramid. Based on this ideological framework, the Nazi regime implemented its horrific plan. Jews, Romani, gays, and everyone else who did not fit into the Nazi ideal were annihilated in the most gruesome manner.[7]

The extent to which the theory of evolution influenced Nazi ideology is controversial.[8] One quote by Hitler may indicate that he resented the idea that he descended from apes. That was presumably an insult to his Aryan project. On the other hand, he repeatedly used evolution to argue for Nazi superiority and the suppression of "inferior" people and nations. In a speech in 1927, he emphasized how the struggle for survival is the driving force of human development: "You are the product of this struggle. If your ancestors had not fought, today you would be an animal. They did not gain their rights through peaceful debates with wild animals . . . but rather the earth has been acquired on the basis of the right of the stronger."

The theory of evolution has been misused to justify some of the worst atrocities in history, often disguised as benevolent medical practices. Against this backdrop, it is highly understandable that many are skeptical when the theory of evolution is applied to explain human health and disease. As a white privileged male interested in the relationship between evolution and cancer, I am therefore aware not to be associated with eugenics and its terrible implications, and I want to be very clear on where I stand regarding this issue: Seeing cancer and other diseases in the light of evolution is not about ranking people based on the idea that some are more valuable than others. On the contrary, with this book I want to express a concern that today's biotechnological development, with cancer research at its center, may result in a new and dangerous type of eugenics in society.

Eugenics and Darwin's theory of evolution are two completely different worldviews. While eugenics is a normative ideology that says how someone thinks the world *should* be, the theory of evolution is a descriptive theory that explains how the world actually works. Eugenics is about selecting or eliminating people based on an idealistic definition of who is the most valuable. The theory of evolution is a scientific principle that explains how humans, and everything else living, evolve in interaction with the environment. It does not differentiate between good or bad traits but points out that some traits survive better in some environments than others. Evolutionary *fitness* is a measure of reproductive success and has nothing to do with somebody's idea of who deserves to live or die. Using the theory of evolution as an argument for sterilizing or exterminating people who are sick or different is as irrational as using the law of gravity as an argument for pushing an unstable person off a cliff. There is no justification in claiming that the person would fall anyway.

Life can be brutal, but that is not an excuse for committing atrocities. We live and die. Animals eat each other. Humans oppress and kill members of their own species. We work and struggle and compete to provide food and security for ourselves and our relatives. That is the way life is. The theory of evolution can be used to understand this struggle for survival. It explains why the tendency for aggression is passed on through the generations. But it also explains why we have developed the ability to empathize and care for others. The theory of evolution is a scientific principle that explains life. It does not say that some people, or animals, are more valuable than others.

THE BUILDING BLOCKS OF LIFE

You may think that we have now moved far away from the topic of cancer. On the contrary, we are right at the heart of the problem. To understand cancer, we must understand where the cancer cells come from and how they develop. Therefore, we must understand evolution. So far, we have clarified some fundamental misunderstandings about what the theory of evolution is all about, and it is time to find out what Darwin really discovered.

Defining the theory of evolution can be surprisingly difficult. It does not describe specific objects or behaviors, like Copernicus's theory of how the solar system is organized. Nor can it be described as a mathematical formula, like Einstein's theory of relativity and the relationship between energy, mass, and the speed of light, $E = mc^2$. The theory of evolution describes a principle for development. It is similar to a computer algorithm and relates to an extraordinary property: It is the theory of things that make copies of themselves.

Life, in the biological sense, is all about reproduction. That is the ability to make more or less accurate copies of oneself. Without reproduction, there is no life. So let us do a little thought experiment. Say that after some trial and error, we have managed to create a small machine that makes copies of itself—a tiny self-replicating machine. In professional terms, an item with such properties is called a *replicator*.[9] It is something that uses energy and materials from its surroundings to create a copy of itself. This new replicator will then do exactly the same. One becomes two; two becomes four; four becomes eight, and so on. If one round of copying takes one day, one month later, the number of replicators will have grown to about one billion ($2^{30} = 1,073,741,824$). After one year, there will be more replicators than there are atoms in the universe, so obviously, this process cannot continue for very long. The world would quickly run out of building materials. The replicators, therefore, soon begin to compete for resources. They must steal "food" from one another, and when everything is eaten, they have to eat other replicators. This may sound brutal, but rephrased in a slightly different manner, our little self-replicating machine has created an ecosystem—just because it makes copies of itself.

To understand how this story will continue to unfold, we must introduce an obvious but essential element to the process: Nothing in life is perfect. The replicators will sooner or later make mistakes, and when one replicator has made an error, this error will be copied to all the descendants. Gradually, families of replicators with different modifications will emerge. Most errors will make the machines less efficient at making copies. Then there will be fewer of these. Occasionally, however, an error will create a more efficient replicator. A little detail may make the replicator better at finding building materials or more efficient at assembling the different parts. This new variant will then increase in number—until an even better one comes along. The best replicators will multiply at the expense of the others, and there will be continuous development toward increasingly better survival machines. That is what Darwin called *survival of the fittest.*

Which variant is the better replicator is dependent on the environment. For example, while one type may be most effective at high temperatures, another may work better in colder conditions. The first type will multiply and spread to warmer areas, while the second will proliferate in cooler regions. Thereby, different replicators evolve in different directions in different parts of the world. Even though there is no plan or premade design, nature constantly chooses the variants that are better adapted to its particular environment. This connection between inheritance and environment is what Darwin called *evolution by natural selection.*

Darwin's theory of evolution is all about replication. But what is the connection between replicators and living organisms? The short answer is DNA. Today, most people know that our genes are encoded in DNA molecules. Many have also heard that the Nobel Prize winners James Watson and Francis Crick discovered DNA. That, however, is not entirely correct.[10] DNA was discovered by the Swiss chemist Friedrich Miescher in the late 1860s and was then analyzed and explored by many different scientists. What Watson and Crick discovered in 1953 was how the DNA molecule acts as a replicator.

At the end of the historic paper that described the molecule's iconic spiral structure, they added the following subtle remark: "It has not escaped our attention that the specific pairing we have postulated immediately suggests a possible copying mechanism for genetic material."[11] This sentence may be the greatest understatement in the history of science. They were really saying that they had solved what is arguably the greatest mystery of life—the mechanism of inheritance.

So, how does this enigmatic mechanism really work? It is as simple as it is ingenious, and as a young scientist, I was almost mesmerized by this powerful concept. With naive enthusiasm, I wanted to share my scientific revelation with others, and one day, while our kids were playing with LEGOs in the bathtub, I got a vision. I realized how I could make a DNA-like replicator—which children can play with and their parents wonder about.

To mimic the building blocks of DNA, I needed magnetic "LEGOs" that would float freely in a hot tub.[12] There should be at least two different types of building blocks, A and B, which should interact according to certain rules. First, they should be able to bind together in long chains in any order of sequence, say AABABBBA. These bindings should be hard to establish, but once they happened, they should be quite stable. Second, the As and the Bs should attract each other as pairs, but only when the water was cold. When it was hot, they should float apart.

From science class, I remembered that magnetism is related to temperature, and after a bit of research, I found a commercially available metal that was magnetic at room temperature but not when it got warmer. Thereby, I could make a simple temperature-dependent binding mechanism. To mimic natural changes in temperature, I set the thermostat so that the swirling hot tub was hot during the day and cold at night. Then I turned on the video camera and waited.

Every night when the water got cold, the A and B blocks formed pairs. During the day, they floated apart, and so it continued. Then one day, three blocks collided at exactly the right angle to form a small chain, ABA. The next night something exciting happened. The three bricks in the chain attracted three free-floating partners, lining them up next to each other. Thereby, they connected to form a new chain with the opposite sequence of the first, BAB. This new chain was thus a complementary "mirror" of the first.

The next day, when the temperature increased, the two chains floated apart—and the process could start over again. Two chains became four, four became eight, and the interactions became increasingly more complicated. One chain connected to two other chains and gave rise to a longer sequence. The different sequences had different physical and magnetic properties and behaved slightly differently. They curled up, clung to each other, and competed for the same building blocks. When a chain became too long, it would break up and "die," and so the process continued.

This weird invention may not sound like much. It was not exactly the Frankenstein monster that came crawling out of the hot tub. Yet, it demonstrated an important principle. How the building blocks formed a chain was initially random, determined by the chaotic and unpredictable currents in the water. But once the first chain was established, something fundamental happened. The sequences started to replicate. They used the energy flowing through the system to make copies of themselves. Information on how to make a specific sequence was passed on from one chain to the next. The experiment thus showed how simple objects can give rise to increasingly more complex replicators. All it takes is a bit of water and energy. In principle, I had demonstrated the spontaneous formation of heritable information with the first ever "LEGO-genes."[13]

There are genes for almost everything. At school, we learn about dominant and recessive genes for eye color and blood type. In the media, we hear about everything from obesity genes and breast cancer genes to IQ genes and gay genes. But what exactly is a gene? On Wikipedia, we can read that the word *gene* has several different meanings. "The Mendelian gene is a basic unit of heredity," while "the molecular gene is a sequence of nucleotides in DNA that is transcribed to produce a functional RNA."[14] Some emphasize that genes are recipes for proteins, while others talk about "the book of life," and it all sounds terribly complicated. The simple fact is that genes are just chains of four different building blocks with the ability to make copies of themselves.

The four building blocks are molecules that have been named A, G, T, and C. They are found predominantly in the cell nucleus and are collectively referred to as nucleotides. When several nucleotides join together as strands, we call it a DNA molecule or just DNA. But the most important point is not what all the different molecules are called. What really matters is what they do.

Like the "LEGOs" in the hot tub, nucleotides can be linked together in long chains in any order of sequence. They have shapes and magnetic properties that make A and T attract each other, as do G and C. A chain of nucleotides will thus attract individual nucleotides that float around inside the cell nucleus. They align along the original chain and are connected to form a new chain. Thereby, the sequence of nucleotides is copied from one chain to the next. Then the two strands detach, and the copying process can start over again—just like it did in the hot tub.

Exactly how the first DNA-like replicators came about, we do not know. The experts discuss whether it started near hot springs on the bottom of the sea or in small ponds that were heated by the sun.[15] But somehow, somewhere, more than 3.7 billion years ago small chains of molecules started to replicate. These were the first genes.

Changes—or mutations—in the sequence of nucleotides produced genes with slightly different properties. Some had a tendency to curl up to make certain structures, while others interacted with different types of molecules. Accordingly, they also had a slightly different ability to replicate. Those that were best at copying themselves in a particular environment increased in number at the expense of others. There were winners and losers, and natural selection led to the evolution of increasingly more advanced copying mechanisms.

While some genes competed for building materials, others teamed up to collaborate. Together they started to manipulate other molecules to their own benefit. They then used these molecules to make structures and tools, which we today know as proteins. Different genes are recipes for different proteins, and many genes get their names from their protein's function. *The hemoglobin* genes, for example, are genes that make proteins that transport oxygen in the red blood cells. The *collagen* genes make proteins that form long fibers to build cartilage and tendons, while the *lactase* gene makes a protein that breaks up the lactose molecules found in milk to use them as energy.

With the help of proteins, the genes could build advanced structures. One particularly useful strategy was to surround themselves and their proteins with a protective membrane of fat molecules. The genes moved into a bubble of fat, and thereby they created the first cell. Groups of genes then began to copy themselves inside these fat bubble cells, and when they were done, they split the cell in two and went their separate ways. This process then continued for several hundred million years, and the oceans were filled with cells.

Some genes evolved to make proteins that transmitted signals between cells, allowing them to communicate and collaborate. Instead of doing everything themselves, cells in the same family started to divide tasks between themselves—like the individuals in an ant colony. While some took the lead, other cells could provide nourishment and protection. Some provided movement, while others were pillars or messengers to support the community. Eventually, complex multicellular organisms evolved, comprising a digestive system, an immune system, muscles, a skeleton, and a hormonal and nervous system that coordinated it all. They became fish, amphibians, reptiles, mammals, and eventually humans.

A human life begins when 23 DNA strands from our mother join up with 23 DNA strands from our father in a zygote. In each cell in our body, there are thus 46 DNA strands that must be copied every time a cell divides. When the copying is done, the long chains bundle up into chromosomes that we can see in a microscope as small, elongated structures within the cell nucleus.

Our body is made up of about 30 trillion microscopic cells, each containing two meters of DNA, consisting of six billion nucleotides. Each time a cell divides, this entire sequence of nucleotides must be copied to the new cells. Thus, there are six billion things that can go wrong for every single cell division, and as we will soon explore, that is exactly why we get cancer.

SELFISH GENES

Through the history of the genes, we are now back to where we started, with the incredible yet fallible human body. The only difference is that when we see the world from this perspective, it is no longer *our* body. Nor are they *our* genes. The genes were first. They developed us, and we are their creatures. We are hyperadvanced cell colonies, evolved through billions of years so that the genes can travel from one generation to the next. We are the genes' means of transportation—their vehicles.

Seeing evolution from the perspective of the genes is commonly known as *the selfish gene theory*,[16] and is largely attributed to the controversial and world-famous biologist Richard Dawkins. His book *The Selfish Gene*[17] was published in 1976 and has revolutionized the understanding of evolutionary biology. But the theory has also met great resistance. Accordingly, the gene-centered perspective to evolution has gained little attention in general education. It is rarely taught in school, and many people have never heard of this transformative way of understanding life.[18]

Personally, I discovered the idea of the selfish gene theory by coincidence in the early 1990s. I was an MD-PhD student at the Oslo University Hospital. It was still the early days of molecular biology, and I had been assigned the task of establishing a small laboratory for identifying cancer-related mutations in different tissue samples. I had just received a top-of-the-line machine for artificially replicating fragments of DNA by a method known as polymerase chain reaction, or PCR.[19] That may sound complicated, but in principle it was just 69 miniature hot tubs for copying DNA in the same way as my previously described "LEGOs."

The PCR machine was in the process of mass-producing a specific gene sequence, which I was later going to analyze for mutations. I was looking for changes in the *K-RAS* gene, a so-called *oncogene* with a critical role in cancer development.[20] K-RAS makes a protein that functions as an on/off button for cell division, and specific mutations lock the switch in the "on" position. The cells are thus continuously signaled to multiply and the mutation involves an important step toward cancer. From the perspective of the mutated K-RAS gene, this effect is quite beneficial, as it copies itself to more and more cells. But as it promotes cancer, the oncogene has no consideration for the rest of the body and may rightly be labeled as *selfish*.

So here I was in my lab, artificially replicating fragments of selfish cancer genes. The radio was on as usual, and while I was sitting there surrounded by selfish DNA sequences, an interesting conversation caught my attention. The journalist was interviewing a biologist about Richard Dawkins's revolutionary perspective on evolution. It was the most transformational idea of my academic life. I had been interested in evolution since primary school, but there were several issues that just did not make sense: Why do animals of the same species fight? Why do humans compete and kill each other? Why do hereditary diseases proliferate in the population? And finally, why do cancer cells spread in the body, even in young people? Obviously, that is not advantageous for either the organism or the species. As if by magic, all the pieces fell into place: Neither the organism nor our species is the purpose of life. Evolution is all about the genes' struggle for existence, not ours. They made us. They are the ones who live on, while our body is simply their means of transportation.[21]

This radical change of perspective can be hard to accept. Science tells us that humans are only one of many stages in the development of life. We live on a small planet, in one of a hundred million solar systems, in one of a hundred billion galaxies. It is difficult to accept our insignificance in the vast universe, and the selfish gene theory tends to reinforce this perspective. Must we also accept that we exist only to pass on genes to the next generation? It is easy to understand that many people perceive such a worldview as strange and absurd. Some may say nihilistic—the belief that life is meaningless.

Like the theory of evolution itself, Dawkins's theory of *the selfish gene* has met strong opposition. Many people have misunderstood the term "selfish" to imply that genes have a will and make conscious decisions. It is, therefore, important to emphasize that the word is used as a metaphor. It is not about selfishness in the human sense. Genes have neither thoughts nor opinions. They are just self-copying sequences of molecules. But precisely because of this ability to multiply and evolve, they are "selfish" in the sense that they compete with each other for energy and building materials. And they have absolutely no regard for what we may think is right or wrong.

Some believe that the theory of the selfish gene justifies selfish actions. That is yet another example of how the theory of evolution is wrongfully perceived as an ideology. Again, we must emphasize that the theory of evolution is descriptive in the same way as the law of gravity. It aims to describe the world as it is, not how somebody thinks it should be. People who believe that the selfish gene theory justifies greed in the stock market[22] have missed this most fundamental aspect of science. Genes compete and collaborate, but they are neither good nor evil. They just replicate whenever the conditions are right.

Richard Dawkins has said he regrets using the word *selfish* because it has generated so much misunderstanding and confusion. In retrospect, he would rather have called it the *immortal* gene.[23] One may wonder if Dawkins and his groundbreaking book would have still become famous. The unique quality of the selfish gene theory is that it sees the world from the genes' perspective, describing how they replicate and develop in interaction with the environment. This self-sustaining property implies a form of molecular selfishness, which is essential to understand the evolutionary process. Yet, it must not be confused with greed or evilness in the personal sense.

The selfish gene theory has also been perceived as an additional threat to religion. Critics argue that the idea aims to replace God as the creator of life, and they misinterpret the metaphor to imply a form of will or consciousness.[24] Again, we must thus emphasize that genes are simply molecules—with the ability to self-replicate. The process is driven by the laws of physics, and there is no higher meaning.

Richard Dawkins responded to the criticism of the theory of evolution and the selfish gene theory with a frontal attack on all religiosities. He shifted his focus of attention from evolution to atheism, and his later book *The God Delusion* concludes that God is a fallacy that exists only in people's minds.[25] That is certainly a legitimate point of view. Dawkins has pointed out how religion and superstition undermine the understanding of science, and he is an uncompromising champion of critical thinking. Yet, we should be careful about dismissing people who believe in God or who are skeptical of the theory of evolution as idiots.

Personally, I tend to have lost my enthusiasm for waging this kind of culture war. Whether God has created the forces of nature, we have created God, or the forces of nature simply are God, we will not resolve—at least not in this book. Still, we know that the forces of nature exist, and we know a lot about how they work. Regardless of where they came from, we can explain the evolution of life on earth, with all its complexity, beauty, and brutality, based on a simple principle of how molecules make copies of themselves.

I praise everybody who fights against religious fundamentalism. I encourage critical thinking and urge opposition to those who seduce and exploit people for profit and publicity. However, when the goal is to spread knowledge and scientific insight, I have more faith in dialogue and respect than in conflict and condemnation. You seldom convince someone by attacking them, and there is little sense in pushing ideas that people are unable or unwilling to understand. On the contrary, research on so-called climate skeptics and anti-vaxxers shows that confrontation usually has the opposite effect. The stronger you try to change their minds, the more certain they are that researchers and authorities are trying to manipulate and deceive them, and the more convinced they become of their own convictions.

The underlying psychology seems obvious. None of us like to be told that we are stupid. We have our own understanding of reality, and from that, we make our opinions and decisions. You cannot force someone to change their mind, and my goal with this book is not to tell people that their understanding of cancer is wrong. I am simply suggesting that there are also other ways to see the problem. Nor do I have the desire to criticize religion or to preach Darwinism. As a matter of fact, I strongly oppose and deliberately avoid the word.

The term Darwinism was introduced by one of Darwin's strongest proponents, his fellow biologist Thomas H. Huxley. Huxley is often referred to as "Darwin's bulldog" and courageously defended Darwin against a flood of unreasonable criticism.[26] Yet, by coining the term Darwinism, he also did Darwin and science a great disservice. The theory of evolution is not an -*ism*. It is not a doctrine or philosophy of life we choose to follow or believe in, like socialism,

Islamism, or Buddhism. We do not call Newton's laws of physics "Newtonism" or the theory of relativity "Einsteinism," and we should not use such terminology to describe the theory of evolution.

The term Darwinism is an unintended gift to those who want to reject the theory of evolution as an ideology. I am not a *Darwinist* because I think the theory of evolution is a powerful tool for understanding life. If anything, I am a scientist. Words matter—also in science. The words we choose shape how we think and understand, and there is always room for interpretation. The message you intend to communicate is not necessarily how it is received, and the best we can do is to share and discuss our views.

The theory of evolution is a scientific model tested and developed through systematic observations and experiments. It becomes increasingly better the more knowledge we add to it, but we can never prove it is true. That is the nature of science. The notion that we do not know the truth separates science from faith and religion. And paradoxically, this fundamental limitation gives science its unique power.

Evolution provides a scientific basis for understanding life on earth. It explains our biological origin, and as we shall see, it can also explain why we get cancer. But as a scientific model, it also has some major limitations. Knowing that we are vehicles for passing on genes to the next generation is hardly relevant for a desperate cancer patient struggling to get through everyday life. That the disease is explained by our evolutionary history is no consolation for parents who worry about losing a child to brain cancer. Scientific understanding does not remove grief and pain. Yet, knowledge is power, and understanding why we get sick and die may provide meaning and comfort in otherwise senseless situations. Seeing cancer in the light of evolution is not the ultimate truth, but it gives us new perspectives, which can help to build a more comprehensive model of understanding.

IN THE LIGHT OF EVOLUTION

How evolution makes sense of seemingly meaningless phenomena may be illustrated by another childhood story. It was a sunny spring day, and all the kids were proudly riding their new bikes around the neighborhood. We eagerly discussed the shiny vehicles and analyzed every little detail—from gears and brakes to bells and lights. We had a pretty good understanding of the purpose and function of the various parts, but one item created wonder and disagreement. What was the point of the tiny rubber hairs on the new bicycle tires? Some claimed that they provided extra grip, especially when riding on the terrain, while others thought they were there to measure the tires' wear. Those who had slightly older bikes argued the hairs would wear down and disappear after just a few trips. So, obviously, they had no function at all.

The rubber hairs on the new bicycle tires seemed to be a mystery, and it was only many years later that I discovered the real explanation. A TV documentary about the making of rubber tires provided the full story. The mysterious hairs were created by tiny air tubes in the molds that shape bicycle tires from liquid rubber. The purpose is to release the air from the mold so that you do not get bubbles in the tires. When all the air is squeezed out, the small tubes also fill with rubber, leading to the formation of the hairy extensions. So, in conclusion, they have no function for riding the bike. Instead, the mysterious phenomenon results from an essential step in the development of the vehicle.

Similar relationships between seemingly meaningless phenomena and the underlying developmental history are also common in biology. What we see does not necessarily have a meaning or purpose here and now but may result from a long evolutionary history. To understand a biological phenomenon like cancer, we must know how organisms have evolved. As Dobzhansky so strikingly wrote, there is absolutely nothing in biology that makes sense unless we see it in the light of evolution.[27]

Many properties of the human body do not seem very logical at first glance. Why we get cancer is one of them, but let us start with something a little easier. Like, what is the point of the human tailbone? We do not have a tail that balances our body when we run or that functions as a fifth limb when we climb, and there is nothing to wag when we are happy. The only time we really think about the tailbone is when we hurt it, and it seems like just a nuisance.

To be correct, the human tailbone does function as support and protection, especially when sitting. Yet only when we see the phenomenon in the light of evolution does it really make sense. The small bone at the bottom of the spine is a remnant from our ancestors who swam in the ocean and climbed trees. Without tails and tailbones, our early forefathers and foremothers would not have survived, and we would not exist.

Similarly, it can be hard to understand the purpose of many genes. Why do we have genes that make us sick? Take, for example, the gene that causes so-called sickle cell anemia.[28] This gene makes the body produce red blood cells that are not round and smooth like they should be. Instead, they are shaped like a sickle. Since people are no longer using sickles to harvest crops, it may be better to say that they are shaped like a new moon. Anyhow, the problem is that these deformed cells tend to break apart, leading to severe anemia.

The cause of this strange disease is a mutated variant of the genes that make hemoglobin, the protein that carries oxygen within the red blood cells. People who get sickle cell anemia have inherited the "broken" gene variant. Or to be specific, they have not only inherited one gene; they have also inherited the same gene variant from both mother and father. People with one mutated and one normal gene are healthy and are said to be *carriers* of the disease.

Another curious phenomenon is that sickle cell anemia is most common in Central Africa, and the distribution coincides almost perfectly with the spread of a completely different disease—malaria. That is not a condition you inherit but is caused by infection with a single-celled organism, a small parasite that is transmitted by blood-sucking mosquitoes. The malaria parasite enters the bloodstream, and after a complicated life cycle, it multiplies inside the red blood cells. And here is the link to sickle cell anemia.

The malaria parasite does not thrive in blood cells containing the mutated form of hemoglobin. The mutated gene provides protection, and even the healthy carriers of the gene have a ten times lower risk of developing malaria than those with only the normal variant. In Africa, where more than one million children die of malaria every year, the sickle cell anemia gene thus provides an evolutionary advantage. Accordingly, this abnormal, albeit protective variant has multiplied and spread throughout the malaria-infested regions of the world. The carriers are protected against malaria, while the price is paid by the children who, unfortunately, inherit the gene in double dosage and get sickle cell anemia.

This intriguing case thus illustrates the value of seeing life in the light of evolution. It explains the otherwise mysterious problem of why so many children in certain parts of the world inherit a deadly blood disease. From our personal perspective, we would expect evolution to favor genes that make us healthy, but biology is more complicated. A deadly gene may protect us from a mosquito-borne parasite.[28]

We often divide genes into good and bad according to how they affect our lives. There are some that do us well and others that make us sick. But the world is not that simple. A gene that makes us morbidly overweight in an affluent society may be vital during a famine. Genes predisposing to destructive and psychopathic personality traits in a normal society may be critical to survival during a brutal war.

Evolution is not about healthy and normal versus sick and abnormal. That is just our interpretation. Evolution always concerns complicated interactions and compromises. When we see the world from the genes' perspective, the best genes are simply the ones that copy themselves most effectively in their given environment. They are molecules and have no regard for our well-being. Successful genes can make us sick, and as we shall see, the gene variants that give us cancer are highly efficient. To understand the disease, we must thus be willing to disregard our egocentric worldview and follow the logic of the genes.

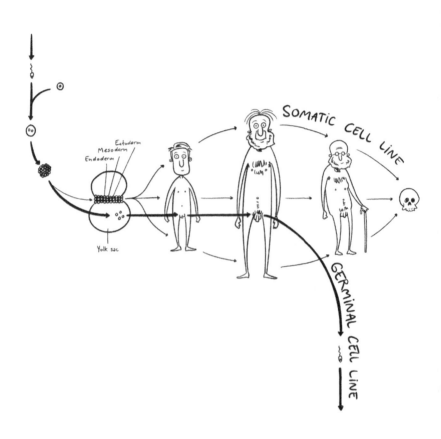

CHAPTER 7

The Evolution

GENETIC CROSSROADS

The human body has evolved through millions of years of evolution, but it also evolves every time a new organism takes shape. To understand how our bodies work, we must figure out how these two processes are related.

The evolution of the species, which has taken billions of years of natural selection, is, in many aspects, repeated during a few weeks of embryonic development.[1] In the early stages of development, we have a tail and gills, similar to a fish embryo. The tail gradually shrinks to become the rudimentary tailbone, while the gills develop into the lower jaw, the throat, and the three small bones—the malleus, the incus, and the stapes—that transmit sound from the eardrum to the inner ear. From the fish stage, we evolve to become more like amphibians and reptiles. Then we become mammals, and like other primates, we develop a large brain and hands for gripping. Finally, we have all the characteristics of our own species, *Homo sapiens*.

So, what exactly is the relationship between the evolution of the species and the evolution of the embryo? The answer lies right in the middle of the fertilized egg cell. The zygote contains all the genes that make a human being, and as we have already explored, the genes' path goes on in two different directions. One copy of the genes follows the germ cells off to the next generation and continues the journey through history. The other copy of the genes is passed on to all the cells in the body. They will continue to replicate for as long as we live but have no future beyond the life of the organism. As previously described, this is somewhat similar to the relationship between the workers and the queen in an ant colony. The genes in the cells of the body do their job and eventually sacrifice themselves to ensure that the genes in the germ cells are passed on to the next generation.

Let us follow the hemoglobin genes as an example. The first variants of these genes appeared several hundred million years ago.[2] And they have since migrated through history, from parents to children, inside the germ cells. For each generation, they have also been copied into all the cells of the body. In the red blood cells they have then made the proteins for transporting oxygen to all the other cells. Without this ability, the body would not function. The hemoglobin genes thus ensure that their own sequence and the sequence of all the other genes are passed on to the next generation.

Each generation, the genes are tested for their ability to create a well-functioning body. A mutation in a gene that prevents the blood from transporting oxygen will quickly perish. Other genes have other vital functions. Some are needed to fight viruses; some provide energy to the muscles, while others make the organism sexually attractive to a partner. The fundamental challenge is to get all the cells to work together to achieve the overall goal of reproducing. The genes have thus evolved numerous mechanisms that make the cells work together as a team—a team of 30 trillion players working together to send an ovum or sperm cell off to the next generation.

One gene plays an especially central role in coordinating this complicated teamwork. Let me introduce *TP53*. It is not a catchy name, but we are talking about one of the greatest celebrities in the gene world. TP53 makes the protein *p53*, which in 1993 was named "molecule of the year" by the famous journal *Science*.[3] This gene and the protein it makes have been featured in over one hundred thousand scientific articles. In 2020, the 40th anniversary of the discovery of TP53 was marked with several news articles, as well as an international conference. TP53 is, in many ways, the genes' answer to Nelson Mandela.

So, what is the reason for this heroic status? TP53 belongs to a family of genes that evolved 800 million years ago. That was the time in evolutionary history when cells began to cooperate in larger units, and the TP53 gene family played a central role in the development of multicellular organisms.[4]

TP53's job is to check that all the genes in a cell are copied correctly. Its protein acts as a sensor that detects damaged DNA, and when this sensor is triggered, it activates a number of different processes. First, cell division is halted so that damaged DNA cannot be copied to new cells. Then other genes and proteins are activated to ensure that the damage is repaired, and if that is not possible, TP53 initiates apoptosis. In other words, the cells with irreparable damage are told to kill themselves. In this way, TP53 ensures that all the genes in all the cells of the body remain accurate copies of their original versions in the zygote. The famous gene has therefore gained the reputation for being the *guardian of the genome*.[5]

TP53 is essential for the function of multicellular organisms. It has survived hundreds of millions of years of evolution and is found in virtually all animal species. Without TP53, DNA damage would spread uncontrollably through the body and result in chaos. I should emphasize, however, that TP53 is only one important example. We have thousands of genes that in various ways ensure that the cells work together to form a functional organism. Many are involved with the regulation of cell division, DNA repair, or apoptosis, but there are also many other essential functions. Some genes regulate the immune system that protects the body against bacteria and viruses. Some ensure that all the cells get the nutrition they need, while others generate the nerve signals that coordinate thoughts and movements. Millions of years of natural selection have led to the development of genes that work together to build a well-functioning organism of enormous complexity.

The cells of our body are genetically programmed to collaborate. So, why do they develop into cancer? Why do some cells go astray and develop into malignant tumors that may kill us? The short and somewhat superficial answer is that although TP53 and other control genes are very good at preventing DNA damage, the process is not perfect. Sometimes even TP53 gets a mutation and the cell runs out of control.

The relationship between sunbathing and skin cancer is an illustrative example. The UV rays from the sun cause DNA damage that may lead to mutations.[6] Such mutations can occur in any gene but are extra problematic if they appear in genes controlling DNA copying and cell division. Loss of control thereby leads to more mutations and generates a chain reaction of DNA damage.

This simple and seemingly logical relationship is how cancer development is often explained to the public. DNA damage leads to gene mutations, which lead to uncontrolled cell division and, eventually, cancer. The American National Cancer Institute website says it like this: "Cancer is a genetic disease—that is, it is caused by changes to genes that control the way our cells function, especially how they grow and divide."[7]

This explanation makes sense and is not wrong, but it misses the most important part of the explanation. Cancer development is not just about genes that get damaged. It is about genes that replicate and evolve. As we have discussed before, this property is what makes genes so special. A gene mutation that ruins a cell so that it dies makes little difference to the body. There are plenty of cells, and the damaged cell will quickly be replaced by a normal cell. The problem occurs when a mutation makes a cell better—better at dividing and surviving in its given environment. Cancer development is all about survival of the fittest inside the body.

EVOLUTION WITHIN

When we talk about evolution, it usually concerns species and organisms developing throughout history. It is basically about the genes' passage within the germ cells, and the path of development is generally referred to as the *germinal cell line* or simply the *germline*. Cancer development, on the other hand, is about how genes evolve inside the body. Since the Greek word for body is *soma*, this path of development is called the *somatic cell line* or simply the *somatic line*.[8]

From the outset in the zygote, the genes in the two cell lines are one and the same. They all come from the historic germline, but then the road divides. One copy of the genes continues on the germline, while the other copy enters the somatic line to make all the cells of the body—splitting up in different directions to make all our different organs. So, in reality, the somatic development is not really a line, but more like the branches of a big tree.

This concept of evolution within the body may sound strange. Yet, it is quite an old discovery. The Danish medical doctor Niels Kaj Jerne described this phenomenon as early as 1955,[9] and 29 years later, he received the Nobel Prize for his revolutionary discovery. Jerne was not a cancer researcher but an immunologist. He studied how the body becomes immune after being infected with bacteria or viruses and how such immunity can also be achieved with vaccines. The details of immunological reactions are incredibly complicated and involve many different genes, proteins, and cells moving within the body. Yet Jerne found that the underlying principle was quite simple.

The fundamental problem is to protect the body from bacteria and viruses. So, let us use the notorious coronavirus as a timely example. As most of us have experienced, the microscopic causes a sometimes severe disease known as COVID-19. The virus itself is often illustrated as a gray sphere with small red antennas, and like other viruses, it is basically a DNA sequence wrapped in proteins. To be precise, the coronavirus consists of a sequence of 29,811 nucleotides, divided into 29 genes, which make different proteins.[10] By injecting these genes into our cells, the virus takes control and uses our body to make millions of copies of itself. Then, as we breathe and cough, they are spread from one person to the next.

The virus keeps making copies of itself, but as we have already discussed, nothing is perfect. New variants—or mutants—occur all the time. Most of the mutants are worse replicators than the original ones and disappear as fast as they come. Occasionally, however, a new variant emerges that is better at copying and spreading than the existing versions. Due to natural selection, this variant will soon dominate and spread throughout the population.

When an opportunity arises, a new variant can also make a jump to another species. That is probably how the corona pandemic started. The virus most likely spread from bats via raccoon dogs to humans, although some believe it may have stopped by a Chinese research laboratory along the way. Anyhow, it got out of control, and we all know how new and more effective corona mutants evolved to conquer the world.

Since new mutants are constantly evolving, it is impossible to know in advance which variants we will encounter during our lifetime. Before the pandemic, we had no genes to protect us from this specific coronavirus. Yet, some genes have developed a technique that solves this fundamental problem. We are talking about the genes that make antibodies. Antibodies are proteins that function as target-seeking missiles, which flow through the body in search of intruders. They are produced by the so-called B cells in the blood and represent a crucial weapon in the body's defense against bacteria and viruses.

So how can genes make antibodies that recognize all the world's viruses and bacteria, including new mutants that have never existed before? The secret is that the antibody genes rearrange their own DNA sequence to make new variants, similar to how we shuffle a deck of cards to make a random poker hand. Accordingly, each B cell ends up producing its own unique antibody. Since we have billions of B cells, we thus have antibodies that can recognize virtually all types of invaders.

From the outset, there is only one cell for each antibody, and the first time we are infected with the coronavirus, only a few B cells make antibodies that recognize that particular mutant. The immune system is thus quickly overpowered and we get sick. But that initiates the ingenious countermeasure. The few cells with antibodies that recognize the virus are stimulated to multiply. They gradually increase in number, and after a few days of sickness, the invader is usually defeated. Moreover, the antibody genes continue to make small changes in their own sequence, and the variants that are best at recognizing the virus get the most stimulated to multiply. The next time the body is infected with the coronavirus, there are thus thousands or millions of cells that are hyperspecialized to fight off this particular variant. The immune system is well prepared and can fight off the next infection without us even noticing. We are immune—until a new variant comes along and the process starts over again.

As Jerne described, this process involves natural selection within the body.[11] The B cells, which make antibodies that recognize a virus, are stimulated to divide faster than other cells. An antibody gene that was generated by shuffling of DNA sequences is thus selected when it encounters a corresponding virus. Then this gene multiplies and lives on in the B cells. In this manner, the antibody genes remember which viruses and bacteria the body has encountered, and the immune system vividly demonstrates how evolution accumulates information about the environment. The genes learn—not individually but as a system that adapts to its environment by natural selection. In general, molecular evolution of genes involves a form of intelligence—a molecular intelligence that existed long before the development of brains and humans.

To understand this process, we need to clarify a few problems. I just wrote that the antibody genes shuffle their own DNA sequence, and the observant reader may have discovered a logical flaw in my line of argument. This ability to change its own sequence does not fit well with the theory of selfish genes, which is all about self-preservation. Genes that change their own sequence to protect the body against viruses do not preserve themselves. On the contrary, they have mutated and become another sequence in order to give the body an effective immune system. That does not sound very selfish.

Here we have stumbled upon a fundamental problem in modern evolutionary theory, which creates a lot of confusion—also in cancer research. We, therefore, need a little clarification. How can the selfish gene theory explain that the antibody genes shuffle their own sequence for the good of the organism? The problem is that we are tricked by looking at just one gene at a time. If we observe more carefully, the genes that make the antibodies do not change their own sequence. Other genes change them. In fact, several genes have evolved to shuffle the sequences of the antibody genes.[12] It is not that the antibody genes are unselfish; it is the other genes that are super selfish. They manipulate the antibody genes to their own advantage, and we can conclude that genes invented genetic engineering long before humans.

That brings us to another common misunderstanding regarding evolution. There is a widespread notion that mutations occur at random, and if they are not random, that is for some reason contrary to the theory of evolution. This is a total misconception. First, it is impossible to make a definite distinction between random and nonrandom mutations. All mutations have a cause. It may be a chemical substance from tobacco smoke, a small glitch in DNA copying, or a gene that modifies the sequence of other genes. Different causes lead to different types of mutations, and we can see traces of both tobacco smoke and copying errors in mutated DNA sequences.[13] Second, there is nothing about the theory of evolution to imply that mutations must occur at random. Natural selection works regardless of how mutations occur. Moreover, as we examine the theory of evolution from the perspective of the genes, it is quite logical that some genes develop the ability to manipulate other genes for their own benefit.

In the course of addressing the fundamental questions, we should also explore the very core of the theory of evolution. The theory states that evolution happens by means of natural selection, but what exactly is selected? What is the unit of selection? Is it the gene, the cell, the organism, groups of organisms, or the entire species? As illustrated by the parable of the blind men and the elephant, what we see depends on where we stand, and to get the full picture, we need to combine different perspectives.

In some contexts, we are interested in how one species has survived while another has become extinct—say the Neanderthals, who ceased to exist about 40,000 years ago while our species persisted.[14] In such situations, it is common to say that evolution has favored or selected one species and not the other. In other contexts, we consider differences within the same species. For example, when an antelope that runs faster than others avoids being eaten by lions. Then we may say that the faster antelopes were selected, while the others, which were eaten, were not selected. Another example occurs when some cancer cells are killed by cytotoxic drugs, while other cells are resistant to the drug and continue to multiply. We would then say that the resistant cells are selected.

We often talk about species, organisms, and cells as entities that persist through generations, but that is not really true. The cells, organisms, and species living today are descendants of but not identical to those that lived in the past. The units that are passed on through the generations are the genes. It is not really the species *Homo sapiens*, the fast antelope, or the resistant cancer cells that are selected. The things—or units—that live on are the genes that make them. While the genes that are not passed on are, by definition, not selected.

The Neanderthals were our closest relatives. Genetically, we are 99.7% identical.[15] As they went extinct and we survived, only 0.3% of the Neanderthal genes have thus been eliminated by natural selection. The vast majority of Neanderthal genes live on in us, but as usual, we are more concerned about differences than similarities. When we talk about Neanderthal genes, we usually refer to the 0.3% that they had and that we are missing. But that is only a part of the story. Genetic analyses show that Neanderthals and humans had sex and exchanged genes throughout their common history. Although the species is extinct, some of the true Neanderthal genes thus live on in us. Accordingly, it is not the species per se that has been selected but a mixture of genes from both species.

When a man and a woman have a child, it is not they as individuals who are selected. For each child, only a random half of each parents' genes are passed on to the offspring. Moreover, some of the genes are mutated. A single nucleotide or a larger segment of DNA may have changed on a gene's path from parent to child. Then it is the mutated version and not the original that is selected. To talk about selection of the organism is thus a gross simplification, which often leads to misunderstandings.

Even cells are not selected as a whole unit. DNA replication is not perfect, and every cell has some slightly different genes. The more mutations, the more inaccurate it is to say that the cell is selected. Although it may be practical to talk about selection of cells, organisms, or species, we must always remember that evolution is really about DNA sequences that are copied and mutated as they wander through history.[16]

That brings us to yet another fundamental question about evolution that we need to clarify in order to understand cancer: Are mutations good or bad? On the one hand, mutations may lead to disease and death. On the other hand, mutations create genetic variation, which is crucial for the development of new species, new traits, and an efficient immune system. So, is it better to have many mutations or few mutations—or is there a middle way?

Again, it is important to see the world from the perspective of the gene, and then the problem becomes quite simple. The most successful genes are, by definition, those that remain stable and multiply through the generations. The purpose is to copy your own sequence as quickly and accurately as possible. A gene that is not able to maintain its own sequence will either become something else or disappear altogether. Accordingly, genetic instability is never good from the perspective of the individual gene. But one gene can benefit from instability in other genes. As we saw for the production of antibodies, some genes can even make other genes unstable for their own benefit. So in conclusion, all genes "want" stability for themselves, but they do not mind instability in other genes.

Things are now starting to get complicated. Some genes replicate and evolve through the germline from one organism to the next. Others branch off to the somatic linage to make all the different cells of the body. They do their job, but sooner or later they all die. Some genes, like TP53, maintain genetic stability, while others promote instability and shuffle DNA sequences. These dynamic relationships are hard to visualize, and now, may be a good time to stop and study the figure at the beginning of this chapter.

Imagine how genes migrate through history in the germline while a copy of the same genes goes off to the somatic line to make all the cells of the organism. Envision how each gene makes small protein machines that control, repair, and manipulate every function of the cell. Then, try to fathom how billions of cells communicate and collaborate to make a functional body. And finally, try to visualize how every gene in every cell may get mutations that give them new properties.

Human biology is immensely complicated, and it is impossible to grasp all the details. Yet, we can understand the basic principles, and the most important scientific principle in this book is how our genes evolve in two different directions. Some follow the germline to the next generation, while others branch off to the somatic line that forms the body. This genetic crossroad, occurring within the first week of gestation, is fundamental to how our body is organized. And it is also our key to understanding cancer.

THE FINAL COUNTDOWN

Let us take a step back to view the big picture. The human body comprises 30 trillion cells, each containing 46 DNA strands of six billion nucleotides. Every time a cell divides, this entire sequence has to be copied. The guardian of the genome—TP53—and many other genes ensure that DNA copying is as accurate as possible. Yet, it is not perfect. Researchers have calculated that, on average, mutations occur every 100,000 nucleotides. Accordingly, every cell division generates thousands of mutations, and what I wrote earlier about all the cells in the body having the same genes is not entirely true. In reality, all the cells in the body are slightly different. Most of the mutations are insignificant, but the older we get, the more times the cells have divided, and the more mutations there will be in each cell.[17] Sooner or later, some cells will get mutations that interfere with vital functions.

A few years ago, cancer researchers Bert Vogelstein and Cristian Tomasetti received international attention for their statistical analysis of what causes mutations in our cells. In particular, they wanted to know how many mutations are due to errors in DNA replication and how many are due to environmental factors. The results showed large variations between organs.[18] In the lungs, for example, most mutations were caused by environmental influence, with cigarette smoking as the main culprit. Conversely, in the brain, which is largely protected from the environment, mutations were primarily attributed to errors in DNA replication.

Overall, Vogelstein and Tomasetti found that more than two-thirds of the mutations in the body were due to replication errors. Fewer than one-third could be attributed to environmental factors, while a few were inherited from the parents.[19] The researchers thus concluded that the majority of the mutations that lead to cancer occurred regardless of how we lived our lives. And they emphatically proclaimed that "most cancer cases are caused by bad luck." This headline was then picked up in newsrooms all around the world. The idea that most cancer just happens by chance was quite sensational and resonated well with the public. It removed much of the personal responsibility many people feel about their disease, and that was also the intention. Vogelstein and Tomasetti wanted to alleviate the unwarranted guilt many cancer patients have about the disease, believing the cancer to be their own fault.

The intention was good, but the backlash from the research community was harsh.[20] Some researchers were critical of the actual research, but the biggest outrage came from researchers invested in cancer prevention. Researchers and health-care providers trying to convince people to stop smoking, eat and drink healthier, put on sunscreen, and be more active were furious. If the general public reads that most cancers are just bad luck, it is easy to imagine that many will ignore the good advice. Although the results were important,

Vogelstein and Tomasetti were thus criticized for promoting their "bad luck theory of cancer."[21]

The word *luck* can mean different things in different contexts, and we should be careful of how we use it, especially when communicating complicated cancer research to the general public.[22] We often say that it is luck when someone wins the lottery since the probability that a particular person will win is very small. But it is not luck that someone wins every time there is a lottery. That is how the system is designed. Similarly, we may say that it is bad luck when a cell in a person's body gets a mutation in TP53 and eventually develops cancer. But it is not bad luck that DNA replication errors occur every time a cell divides. That is also how the system is designed—by evolution.

There is no perfect way to copy six billion nucleotides in a small cell. The process can always become a little more accurate. But that will require more time and energy and is not necessarily more efficient from the perspective of the gene. It is not bad luck; it is utterly predictable that there will be more mutations and more cancer the older we get.

Vogelstein and Tomasetti's "bad luck theory of cancer" does not imply that cancer comes out of nowhere, although it may easily be interpreted that way. Instead, their results clearly demonstrate that cancer development is a predictable consequence of how the body is organized.[23] Our cells are genetically programmed to cooperate, but with every cell division, this program accumulates new mutations. The clock starts ticking on the day of conception and continues for as long as we live. As we have already discussed, somatic cells have a limited life span. They are "worker ants" that will eventually expire, and some genes have evolved to keep track of this countdown. And at the center of it all, we find no other than TP53.

The 46 DNA strands that make up our chromosomes need to be strictly controlled, and they have several mechanisms to achieve this goal. One involves a special nucleotide sequence— TTAGGG—which is repeated hundreds of times at the end of each strand. These so-called *telomeres* attract specific proteins to form a neat ending to the chromosomes. Thereby, they function some-what similarly to the splices that sailors make at the end of a rope to keep it from fraying.[24]

The telomeres are essential for maintaining the integrity of the chromosomes but also have another critical function: Every time a cell divides, the telomeres get a little shorter. Eventually, the fraying chromosome ends begin to create problems. That signals to TP53 that something is wrong, and the guardian of the genome steps in and activates the necessary measures. Cell division is put on hold, and if the problem is too great, the cell is sent to apoptosis. Its path has come to an end, and it kills itself.

The telomeres thus function as a clock that counts down toward the end of life. This life, begins as a zygote with new, long telomeres. But for every cell division, they become a little shorter. After about 60 rounds, they are used up. The cells' expiration date has passed. They have accumulated too many mutations and should be sent to apoptosis before they develop into cancer. Life eventually comes to an end, and the telomeres' timekeeping is an unmistakable mark of our temporary existence. The fact that the body ages and dies is not a mistake. It is part of the genes' strategy to copy themselves from one generation of organisms to the next.

EVOLUTION OF CANCER

Our genes have evolved a cunning strategy. First, they program our cells to cooperate to create a multicellular organism that takes them to the next generation. Then, when the job is done, they have programmed the cells and the organism to die.

The goal of these genes is to be passed through the germline from one generation of organisms to the next. But what is the goal of the genes that evolve in the somatic line? What drives the development of genes that replicate and mutate inside the body? As for all genes, there is only one goal—to get copied. That is what genes do. That is the reason for their existence. The best gene—or replicator—in a given environment outcompetes those that are less efficient.

Genes in the somatic line will not be passed on to the next generation. Accordingly, they are not selected because of their ability to make the cells collaborate. On the contrary, their success depends on the ability to multiply as efficiently as possible inside the body. They do not know that such behavior will lead to cancer and eventually kill the organism. They are still just chains of nucleotides copying themselves whenever the conditions are right.

A unique feature of this somatic evolution process is that the somatic cells start with the "brakes on." While single-celled organisms, such as bacteria and amoebae, divide as soon as they have the opportunity, the cells of multicellular organisms are subject to strict control. They are programmed to collaborate and divide only when it benefits the whole organism. Accordingly, natural selection will favor mutations that break free from this suppression. The most successful genes in the somatic lines are those that disengage the checks and balances so the cells can multiply without restrictions. One may say that the somatic cells have an evolutionary drive to become more like single-celled organisms.

Once again, TP53 represents the key example. The guardian of the genome controls both DNA repair and cell division. Thereby it prevents cells from multiplying freely within the body. Cells that somehow get rid of TP53 will thus have an advantage, and that is exactly what happens. About half of all cancers have mutations that incapacitate TP53. The guardian of the genome is either mutilated or ditched so that the remaining genes can multiply freely.[25] Without TP53, nothing stops the cells from dividing, even though they have DNA damage. Nothing activates apoptosis because the telomeres have expired. The brakes are off, and other genes can continue to copy themselves indefinitely.

Again, I should emphasize that in reality things are a bit more complicated. Mutation of TP53 is just one important example of new genetic variants that are selected during cancer development. Hundreds of different genes are activated or deactivated by mutations as cancer progresses, and they all play different parts in the process. Some mutations release the brakes that control cell division, while others lock the gas pedal in the down position. Mutations in the previously mentioned K-RAS, for example, involve a constant signal that stimulates the cell to divide and proliferate.

Other mutations make the cancer cells invisible to the immune system, while some manipulate normal cells to make blood vessels that supply the cancer cells with oxygen and nutrients. As natural selection favors genes that make the cells multiply more freely, cancer cells with new mutations gradually outcompete more restrained variants. The cells grow uncontrollably, and the disease becomes increasingly more aggressive.

Since cancer cells evolve from the body's normal cells, the evolutionary process does not need to start from scratch. The cells already have thousands of genes that may be useful to a cancer cell. The tools are already there, and instead of developing completely new genes, cancer cells often evolve by assembling existing genes in new combinations. Accordingly, one of the most striking characteristics of cancer cells is that they are genetically unstable. When TP53 and other control genes are out of the way, the chromosome structure breaks apart. The 46 DNA strands inside the cell nucleus start to break and reconnect. New cells appear with new combinations of genes, and natural selection favors the combinations that are best fit to multiply inside the body.[26]

My personal interest in the evolution of cancer was triggered by a curious relationship in my own research data, concerning mutations and the location of cancers inside the body. I was collaborating with a research group that had collected tumor samples from 250 different patients with cancer in their large intestines, generally referred to as bowel cancer or, more scientifically, colorectal cancer.

My research project was technically about identifying gene mutations in cell samples collected from these cancers. Indirectly, however, it was a study about the lives of the 250 individual patients. The DNA samples came from the bodies of people who had lived different lives in different environments. Everyone had, in various ways, discovered a tumor in their intestines. Some had seen blood in their feces, some experienced stomachaches, and others had just felt increasingly weak and tired.

Concurrently, the DNA samples concerned the development of 250 different tumors, each representing a colony of living cancer cells. These cells had also lived different lives—inside different patients, in different parts of the bowel. They had their individual story of origin, and the lives of the patients and the lives of the cancers were somehow intricately connected.[27]

The bowel starts at the bottom right side of the abdomen. It goes up toward the liver, below the stomach, and down on the left side before ending in the rectum. Each segment has its own characteristics, and my DNA analysis revealed a curious relationship. The cancer cells that developed in the first segment of the bowel had different types of mutations than those that developed in the last segment. There were several differences, but the most striking was that cancer cells from the last part of the bowel often lacked TP53 and had unstable chromosomes.

Conversely, cancer cells from the first part of the bowel had mutations in another type of DNA repair and control gene.[28] These so-called MMR genes make proteins that repair defects in repetitive DNA sequences. Such sequences, where the same order of nucleotides is repeated in succession, are spread throughout the genome. They are found in the previously described telomeres but also in and around many important genes. Mutations in the MMR genes thus result in cells that lack the ability to repair such repetitive sequences, resulting in a particular type of genetic instability.

So why do cancer cells that develop in the first part of the bowel get mutations in MMR genes that repair repetitive DNA sequences? And why do cells in the last part of the bowel get mutations in TP53 and develop chromosome instability? I seemed to have stumbled upon a little scientific mystery, and with my head filled with ideas about evolution and selfish genes, I became increasingly fascinated by this intriguing problem. I started to read everything I could find about mutations and bowel cancer. What types of chemicals cause what types of DNA damage? How are such damages repaired in the cells? Are there other differences between cancers in the first and last segment of the bowel? Is there a connection between the mutations in the cancer cell and the foods we eat? Last but not least, how could all this be related to the theory of evolution? I felt a bit like Charles Darwin on a journey of discovery—not on the great oceans but inside the human body.

It was a jigsaw puzzle with many missing pieces, and both my patience and self-confidence were put to the test as my PhD funding was running out. How much time could I spend trying to solve a problem nobody else was aware of? Fortunately, I found some pieces that began to form a larger picture, and I started to develop a strong interest in feces.

There seemed to be a connection between the bowel content and the type of genetic instability we observed in cancer cells. Several studies showed that cancer in the first segment of the bowel is somehow related to *bile*. That is the foul-smelling liquid that gives odor and color to poop. The bile acids are produced in the liver and stored in the gallbladder before being excreted into the small intestine. There, they help dissolve fatty food so it can be absorbed by the body. The bile acids then continue to the large intestines, where they are largely absorbed by the blood and circulated back to the liver. The closer one gets to the rectum, the less bile is thus left in the bowel.

In addition, several studies had found an association between bile acids and cancer in the first segment of the bowel. Cancer in the last segment, on the other hand, was more strongly associated with food. As previously discussed, charcoaled sausages and scorched gingerbread cause mutations, and eating such substances increases the risk of bowel cancer. Combined there seemed to be a relationship between the chemical environment in the bowel and the type of genetic instability in the cancer cells.

Other studies showed that bile acids and food carcinogens cause different types of DNA damage. While bile acids cause DNA damage that is recognized and repaired by the MMR genes, food carcinogens cause DNA damage that is recognized by TP53 and other genes that maintain the chromosome structure.

The strange thing was that the cancer cells seemed to have lost the control mechanism that protected them from the harmful environment in which they had developed. Why had the MMR genes been inactivated in the first segment of the bowel, in an environment with lots of bile acids? That is where they should be needed the most. And why had TP53 been inactivated in the last segment of the bowel? This segment is especially exposed to food carcinogens, which cause the type of DNA damage that TP53 has evolved to prevent. The relationship was exactly the opposite of what would be expected. It did not make sense—unless I saw it in the light of evolution.

Evolution by means of natural selection does not have a higher meaning. It is simply about genes being copied or not in the given environment. TP53 assures that the cells of the body function as an integrated organism. It functions as a break, especially in cells with

DNA damage, and the other genes will have an advantage if this guardian of the genome is removed. Thereby, the cancer cells can multiply freely within the body. The same logic applies to the MMR genes. These genes are an obstacle to cell division in an environment with lots of bile acid and mutations that remove their function, giving the cancer cells an advantage.

My discovery that cancer cells from the first segment of the bowel lacked MMR, while those in the last segment lacked TP53 could thus be explained by natural selection. The cancer cells apparently adapted to their environments by losing different control genes, resulting in cancers with different types of genetic instability.

The pieces thus seemed to fall into place. The difference in genetic instability in different parts of the large intestines could be explained by evolution inside the body, and it seemed like I was on the trail of something important. Together with my supervisor, Gustav Gaudernack, I sent the results of three years of pondering to a well-known research journal, and the editor response was overwhelmingly positive.[29]

My theory about the evolution of cancer was quickly published, and soon after, I received a friendly email from a guy named Bert. He congratulated me on the article and described the theory as very thought-provoking. After a quick Google search, I realized that the sender was no other than Bert Vogelstein—the renowned researcher who, to a large extent, had developed the modern theory of cancer development and who has often been cited as a candidate for the Nobel Prize. It was also the same Vogelstein who would later make waves by saying that cancer is 70% bad luck.[30]

It turned out that Vogelstein's research group was testing my theory using genetically engineered cancer cells. These cells had been genetically stabilized but still multiplied vigorously in the laboratory. Vogelstein and his coworkers' idea was then to expose these cells to the type of chemicals found in the bowel. Some of the cells were grown in a dish with a known food carcinogen, while others were grown with a carcinogen similar to bile acids.[31]

The results were striking: The original, genetically stable cells gradually disappeared, while cells that continued to multiply were genetically unstable. They had lost the important control mechanisms and could grow freely in the mutagenic environment. Moreover, there was a clear relationship between the carcinogen they were exposed to and the type of genetic instability they developed. The food carcinogens favored cells with unstable chromosomes, while the bile carcinogens favored cells with instability in repeated DNA sequences. The prestigious research group thus confirmed my theory that DNA-damaging environments favor cells that lose the ability to repair the damage.[32]

The result seemed like a big paradox, and the theory was difficult to explain, even in scientific terms. When I was asked to present the theory in the *Proceedings of the National Academy of Science USA*, I therefore decided to illustrate the evolution of cancer as a car race—the Cell Cycle Grand Prix.[33] Just like in Formula 1, the goal is to get around the racetrack—or the cell cycle—as quickly as possible. Anyone familiar with motorsport knows that can be a daunting task involving complex trade-offs between many different factors. How much can you push the engine? How hard and for how long should you brake? How often should you change tires, and how much time should you spend on maintenance and fine-tuning? Frequent inspections and repairs cost time and resources, while less maintenance results in poor performance and increased risk of accidents.

It is easy to think that more damage requires more repairs, but that is not necessarily correct. Let us assume that the racetrack is quite extreme—that the race goes through a war zone where guerrillas are shooting at the cars as they drive by. To stop the car and open the hood to repair the damage may not be such a good idea. On the contrary, it is better to drive on, even if the engine is coughing and the gearbox is about to break.

This may seem like a far-fetched analogy, but it becomes clearer if we imagine the life of a cell in the lung of a heavy smoker. This cell is continuously bombarded with DNA-damaging chemicals. Accordingly, TP53 stops it from dividing and initiates DNA repair. But as one damage is repaired, a new one appears. The cell gets caught in a futile loop of repair and ends up committing suicide by apoptosis. A cell that loses TP53 will thus have an advantage, and that is exactly what we see: Lung cancers, especially among smokers, very often lack the function of this vital gene. The guardian of the genome has been kicked out, and my somewhat counterintuitive theory may be condensed to a simple wisdom: "Don't stop for repairs in a war zone!"

So let us summarize the evolutionary dynamics of cancer development: A few days after conception, the genes from the zygote go two separate ways. One copy continues to the next generation through the germline, while another branches off to the somatic line to make all the cells of the body.[34] These germline genes program the cells to collaborate, but mutants that break away from the collaboration will have an advantage. Every cell division generates new mutations, and natural selection favors the renegades that develop into cancer.

The somatic cells thus have two possible fates. The first option is to retain the control mechanisms and listen to the organism's needs. These cells will eventually slow down and perish by apoptosis. They have done their job, the germ cells are off to the next generation, and the body withers like a flower in autumn. That is aging.

The second option is to lose the control mechanisms and multiply freely within the body. TP53 and other control genes are thrown out, and the cells become genetically unstable. One mutation leads to another, and natural selection favors the most rebellious variants. That is cancer.

Either way—aging or cancer—we are doomed. But this gloomy fact is neither due to evilness nor bad luck. The cause of cancer is a fundamental consequence of the way we reproduce ourselves, with a distinct division between the germline and the somatic line in the first week of embryonic development. We are temporary cell colonies made by our genes to pass them on to the next generation.[35]

CHAPTER 8

The Synthesis

EPIGENES

We have now established that cancer development involves natural selection of mutated genes within our body. But genes do not provide the full explanation. Cell biology concerns a mind-boggling system of molecules, and it is easy to get confused. To avoid this confusion, I have so far omitted an essential problem. It concerns one of the greatest mysteries in biology and is crucial to understanding multicellular organisms, including our own body: How do cells, which start out with exactly the same genes, develop in many different directions?

All of our cells are descendants of the zygote and have inherited the same genes. Nevertheless, a skin cell is categorically different from a nerve cell, which are both different from a liver cell. How do these differences arise, and how are they maintained throughout life? How does a skin cell know that it is a skin cell?

Despite everything we have discussed concerning gene mutations, these differences between our normal cells are not due to changes in the nucleotide sequence. Instead, the genes have developed another method for cells to evolve within the body—a system that allows genes to be turned on and off when needed. We are talking about the mysterious concept of epigenetics—a type of inheritance that occurs "on top of" the genes.

In simple terms, a gene that is turned on makes a protein with a certain function, while a gene that is turned off does nothing. We have previously discussed how the genes work together to create the body. They have different roles and have developed an advanced system for the division of labor between organs and cell types. Red blood cells, for example, transport oxygen to all the other cells. Accordingly, they need to turn on the gene that makes the hemoglobin protein that is specialized for absorbing oxygen in the lungs and releasing it in the other tissues.

Most other cells do not need hemoglobin, and the gene is turned off. In fact, most genes in a cell are turned off. They do nothing and are simply going for a ride. Only a selection of genes in a cell is activated to make proteins, and these genes determine the cell's characteristics. Cells with exactly the same genes may thus have very different properties.[1]

So, how is this gene regulation established? How do cells know which genes to turn on or off to become, , nerve cells? And how do cells remember this information when they divide in two? How is it copied?

This cellular memory used to be a great mystery, but over the last decades, there has been a revolution in understanding. It concerns small molecules that are added to the DNA strands in specific places. These so-called methyl groups are especially common in the first regulatory part of genes and are generally referred to as DNA methylation.[2]

The relationship between genes and DNA methylation may be best described with a metaphor. Let us say that the genes are words in the recipes for building cells. Then DNA methylation is small markings in the text that say something about how this recipe should be read in different circumstances. If we take the metaphor a little further, we may say that the genes are the script for a play, while DNA methylation is markings in the text about how the performance should be acted out in a particular setup. This variation is not encoded in the play's genes but in the director's and the actor's markings between the lines. It is written in the epigenes.

An epigene is a particular pattern of DNA methylation, just like a gene is a pattern of nucleotides. They are found in all cells but are almost completely wiped out in the zygote. One may say that we start life with a clean script, without scribbles between the lines. Then, during the first days and weeks of development, new DNA methylation patterns are established. Genes are turned on and off, and the epigenes determine whether a cell develops into a liver cell, a blood cell, or any other cell type.

Precisely what determines which genes are methylated in which way is subject to much research, but it is somehow related to the cells' immediate environment. Cells sense how they are positioned in relation to other cells, and a cell located in the middle of the embryo receives other signals than those found on the outside. Depending on how a cell is positioned, it receives signals to form certain epigenes. Thereby the cell develops in a specific direction, for example, to become a muscle cell. There is still a lot we do not know, but in principle, DNA methylation explains how a lump of genetically identical cells develops in different directions.

Once an epigene has been established, it is copied from one cell to the next through cell division.[3] This process is ensured by a gene that makes proteins that function as copying machines. Their task is to copy DNA methylation from one DNA strand to another. Each time a new DNA strand is copied, these proteins check for DNA methylation on the original DNA strand. They then add a similar pattern of DNA methylation to the new strand. Thereby, the epigenes are maintained from one cell to the next. So, when a cell in our body divides, not only is the script of the play copied but also the markings between the lines. In essence, we have discovered the code for writing between the lines in the play of life.

DNA methylation is a new code on top of the genetic code, which allows the cells to evolve in different directions. It is a coding scheme that the genes have developed to control the development of multicellular organisms, and like everything else in the body, the epigenes are carefully regulated. Many genes ensure that DNA methylation is established and copied correctly. Yet, epigenes are much more dynamic than genes and are easily affected by environmental influence. Vitamin B, for example, is one of the main requirements for DNA methylation, and vitamin B deficiency can lead to errors during the formation of the epigenes. That may lead to birth defects, especially a serious condition due to incomplete formation of the spine, known as *spina bifida*. And that is why all women should take vitamin B supplements before and during pregnancy.[4]

In the same way environmental factors may cause mutations in genes, they also cause mutations in epigenes. Some are due to a lack of vitamin B, but many other environmental factors also affect DNA methylation. A mother's alcohol use—or even severe mental stress—may prevent normal formation of epigenes during embryonic development. Errors also occur during the copying process, just like the errors that occur during DNA replication. So, similar to how our cells constantly acquire genetic mutations, they also accumulate epigenetic mutations with increasing age.

That brings us back to cancer. Since the epigenes regulate the genes, they also influence the cells' ability to multiply. An epigenetic mutation that causes a cell to divide faster will increase in number at the expense of others. DNA methylation is an indirect manner for manipulating the genes, and the same way TP53 and other control genes are inactivated by genetic mutations, they are also turned off by epigenetic mutations.[5]

So, let us put this new knowledge in perspective: The genes program the cells in the body to cooperate. At the same time, they have created a system of epigenes for the cells to develop in different directions in interaction with the environment. Both these systems are prone to mutations, and natural selection will favor new variants to make the cells grow faster and more unruly. The result is cancer, and we can conclude that cancer development is an evolutionary process concerning not one, but two different systems of replicators.[6]

But there is more: Recent research shows that our cells have yet another coding system. This code consists of small modifications to the proteins that pack the DNA strands into chromosomes. The proteins are called histones, and the system has been named the *histone code*.[7] There is evidence that these modifications are copied and mutated during cell division, and we can deduce that such "histogenes" are also subject to natural selection. Although much is still unclear, we can thus be reasonably sure that also the histone code plays a role in cancer development.

In conclusion, the field of epigenetics is no longer a vague phenomenon used to label everything in biology we do not understand. Instead, it concerns molecular codes that carry information on top of and alongside the genetic code. Our mental model of life is increasingly more complex, but the fundamental principle remains the same. It only makes sense in the light of evolution.

MEMES

Biology involves codes of molecular information that are replicated, mutated, and selected in dynamic interactions with the environment. The discovery of these replicators has been a painstaking endeavor involving centuries of scientific research. One type of replicator, however, is so common and obvious that it is easy to overlook.

Most people of today are familiar with the concept of memes and how they are spreading on the internet.[8] It may be a particular image, often with a short text, copied repeatedly to convey a specific message or feeling. It could be a celebrity with a unique facial expression, a container ship stuck in the Suez Canal, or a funny kitten. Memes have a message that, for some reason, triggers people to pass them on, like viruses through the population. We say that the meme "goes viral."

Fewer people know that the term meme was invented, or at least defined, by Richard Dawkins—the same person who wrote the book and defined the theory of the selfish gene.[9] Dawkins coined the term meme as an analogy to the concept of the gene. A meme is defined as a unit of cultural inheritance in the same way that a gene is a unit of biological inheritance. Accordingly, memes are not just the typical internet phenomenon. They are all types of ideas, thoughts, or behaviors copied between people—from one brain to the next—everything from melodies and dances to words and knitting patterns.

Such cultural inheritance is not unique to humans. Songbirds mimic each other's tunes, while more intelligent animals like dolphins and primates can imitate more advanced skills. Young chimpanzees, for example, learn from their mothers how to use a sponge of moss to collect rainwater.[10] Mimicry is seen in many different animals, but no other species has developed the ability to the extent of *Homo sapiens*. We imitate and communicate from birth to death, and modern humans are generally more concerned about passing on memes than genes.

It is also evident that memes are subject to mutations. They constantly change and may occur in many different versions. Imagine how the same word exists in different variants in different languages, how a melody can be expressed as different forms of music, or how an image can be re-created in different versions. Take, for example, the painting *The Scream* by Edvard Munch—arguably Norwegian culture's most successful meme of all time. This unique expression has spread to every possible media, from Munch's four original paintings to posters, movies, T-shirts, fridge magnets, and much more. An expression that originated in the brain of a gifted artist has replicated and mutated in many different directions. It has become part of humanity's cultural heritage—a persistent unit of inheritance in our common *memome*.

Memes replicate and mutate. Accordingly, Dawkins logically deduced that they also evolve by means of natural selection. Ideas, songs, or fashions, which for some reason copy themselves more efficiently in a particular environment, increase in number and outcompete others. An illustrating example is how English words are replacing Norwegian ones in everyday language and even more so in academic discourse. Another example is how different pop songs are competing on the charts, spreading through the global population in a matter of days. *Survival of the fittest* obviously also applies to memes.[11]

Biological and cultural information have more in common than we may think. In the same way that a gene gives rise to proteins that produce a particular characteristic, or phenotype, a meme may give rise to artifacts that become a cultural phenomenon. While genes come together to make cells and organisms, memes unite to form stories and theories. Melodies become songs and symphonies, while words and sentences become novels and textbooks. Smaller fragments become larger complexes. Some memes fit together and collaborate, while others compete and exclude each other. The best combinations spread and continue to develop. Those that are less efficient gradually die out. Everything we call culture, from literature and craftwork to religions and scientific theories, can be explained by natural selection of memes. Even our identity and consciousness may possibly be explained in the light of memetic evolution.

Many are critical of this evolutionary perspective to culture.[12] Applying the principles of biology to explain phenomena traditionally belonging to the humanities and social sciences challenges one of the most fundamental cultural barriers in society. Moreover, the idea of *memetic evolution* challenges the perception of what it means to be human to an even greater extent than genetic evolution. It questions the religious concept of the divine soul, as well as the humanistic dogma of free will. If our body is made by genes and our soul is made by memes, then who are we?

As always, it is difficult to accept that we are not the purpose and meaning of life. To integrate biological and cultural information into one scientific model is a daunting task that will continue to meet strong resistance. Yet, it provides a new perspective to our own existence that may help us see life, death, and cancer in a different light.

DARWIN'S THEORY OF INFORMATION

Cancer concerns both body and soul, and to see the whole picture, we need a scientific framework that combines this duality of life. Historically, however, that is not how we usually see the world. The idea that our identity is independent of the body is deeply rooted in religion. Whether we are talking about heaven or hell, Valhalla or reincarnation, the soul magically lives on after our physical death, and our thoughts and ideas have traditionally belonged to the metaphysical world.

Today, modern science is providing a new understanding. Our thoughts and ideas exist as molecular patterns and electric signals in our brains. But they also exist in the brains of those with whom we have shared them. Similarly to how we build mental models of ourselves, we make mental models of other people—especially those we love. These avatars are somehow physically encoded in our networks of neurons, and we do not need to resort to the supernatural to explain the experience that our loved ones live with us, even after they are dead. To quote the Old Norse poem Hávamál, "The word about you never dies."[13]

The memes about us may live on independently of the brain. Many influential people have been made immortal through history books, biographies, and movies. Others have produced art and science. Charles Darwin lives on by virtue of his life's work on the theory of evolution. Adolf Hitler and his National Socialism live on as a grim warning, but, unfortunately, also an inspiration to some. Most people leave weaker footprints, but anyone who has conceived a thought and passed it on has contributed to the memetic evolution of human culture.

Body and soul may appear as two separate domains, but it is also easy to see the connections, especially when it comes to health and illness.[14] Old wisdom, but also new research, shows how physical activity promotes mental health. Few have said it better than the Danish philosopher Søren Kierkegaard: "Above all, do not lose your desire to walk. Every day, I walk myself into a state of well-being and walk away from every illness. I have walked myself into my best thoughts, and I know of no thought so burdensome that one cannot walk away from it."[15]

We have all experienced how mental stress is passed on to the body as tense muscles or restless legs. Stressful thoughts activate complex hormonal systems, which also affect the immune system, and we are more likely to catch a cold when we are mentally exhausted. Mental depression may cause people to eat poorly, be physically inactive, or smoke more, and bad thoughts can literally make us sick.

Body and soul are connected, but what exactly is the connection? What is the common denominator for biological and cultural evolution? Whether we are talking about biology, culture, genes, epigenes, or memes, one concept always comes up—information. It is a word we use all the time, and everybody knows what it means—until we are asked to explain it.

It is natural to think of information as something related to humans, but genetic and epigenetic information existed long before *Homo sapiens* walked the earth. Genes have copied information for billions of years and developed cells and organisms that are much more complex than anything humans have created. Even memes existed before there were humans. The first songbirds evolved over 50 million years ago,[16] and brains, which can process and pass on information, are not unique to our species. We did not invent information. Information invented us.

So what is information?[17] A physicist or computer scientist would probably say that information is related to *entropy*, an entity that may be described by different mathematical formulas. In more simple terms, entropy is a measure of how things are organized. If something is scattered and chaotic, it has high entropy, while something that is densely packed and well organized has low entropy. The universe once started as something small and compact, with extremely low entropy. It exploded with a big bang and has continued to expand. The galaxies are moving farther and farther apart. Things shatter, age, and weather, and everything tends to disintegrate if it is not somehow actively counteracted.

One of the most fundamental laws of nature, the second law of thermodynamics, states that the entropy of a finite system always increases. In other words, there is always more disorder and chaos. This constant increase in entropy gives direction to the universe. It is related to how events happen in order and how time goes forward, not backward. Why the world is organized like this is difficult to explain, but something else would have been strange. On the other hand, if we lived in a world where everything went backward, we would probably have thought that was completely normal as well.[18]

Anyhow, the entropy in the universe increases, and everything becomes more disorganized over time. Here on earth, however, we can see with our own eyes that the entropy is decreasing. Things are becoming more organized. Molecules become cells, cells become organisms, and organisms become societies. We build houses that become cities and create technology that connects everything in a giant network. The entire planet is covered by a layer of life that is becoming increasingly advanced and integrated. So how is it possible that life on earth becomes more organized while the laws of physics say that the entropy in the universe always rises?

The answer is not that difficult: Thermodynamics says that the entropy in a separate system always rises, but the earth is not a separate system. We are literally in a system with the sun—the solar system. Life on earth lives off the energy released by our local star. And as demonstrated by my magnetic "LEGOs" in the hot tub, genetic information can arise and evolve due to simple temperature fluctuations. Simple molecules combine to form self-replicating chains. They pick up building materials from their surroundings, build copies of themselves, mutate, and evolve by means of natural selection.

The process is driven by energy released from the sun as it slowly burns out. The entropy of the solar system, and the universe at large increases, while life on earth represents a small bubble of order and organization. Accordingly, there is no contradiction between the laws of physics and the complexity of biology.

The concepts of entropy, energy, information, and life are related in a complex manner, described in thick textbooks of physics, chemistry, and molecular biology. Yet we all know how it works in practice. Life is generally about solving problems, and there are basically two ways to do it. Say the problem is getting through a locked door. You can either use a lot of energy to break through it, or you can solve the problem with information. For that, you need a key. The point of a key is that it contains information. It has a pattern that fits the mechanism in the lock so the door can be opened almost without energy. Information is simply a pattern that matches another pattern.

This explanation also fits well with the modern scientific understanding of information. Information is defined as shared entropy between two systems. In other words, it is a pattern in one place that corresponds to a pattern in another place.[19] That is why information is so difficult to explain. It is not one thing but two—two independent things that are copies of each other. Accordingly, information arises when something is copied, such as when a nucleotide sequence first replicated itself somewhere in the primordial sea.

Then we may ask, "What was that information about?" At first, it was just about how to copy this nucleotide sequence. Thereby, the information on how to make this sequence spread out in different directions. Through mutations and natural selection, new sequences emerged that were particularly good at copying themselves in a particular environment. These sequences thus gathered information about the environment in which they had evolved. As the nucleotide sequences began to organize amino acids into proteins, they also began to contain information about how to make proteins with different functions. In this way, more and more information was stored in the genes. And we can see how evolution creates information.

It is easy to think of information as something fleeting and abstract that exists independently of the physical world. That is a fundamental misconception. One of the most important realizations in modern science is that information always has a physical substrate. "Information is physical," wrote the famous physicist Rolf Landauer, who thereby defined a new and integrated understanding of science.[20]

Landauer was particularly interested in physics and information technology, but his basic understanding is equally relevant for biology and the life sciences. Information is copied from molecule to molecule, from cell to cell, and from organism to organism. It flows through our bodies, and we are, first and foremost, complex information systems.

With regard to cultural information, the physical substrate may seem somewhat unclear, but memes are also patterns that are copied and transformed from one physical medium to another. A melody we have learned is somehow stored in our brain, and when we share it with others, it must first be translated into electrical nerve signals. From there, it is translated into movements in the larynx or the fingers that play on a musical instrument, turning into the waves of air pressure that we call sound. The same melody can also be turned into notes on paper, bits on a hard disk, or electromagnetic signals that move at the speed of light between our mobile devices. From there, it can again be converted into pressure waves, which in somebody's ears become new nerve signals. The circle is closed, and unless there was a mutation along the way, the original melody has reached another brain.

Life, in all its forms, is about information. This information is always physical, but the point is not the physical objects themselves. The same pattern can be copied and converted between different media. Nucleotide sequences can become new nucleotide sequences, but they can also be translated into sequences of amino acids that become proteins. The proteins can create chemical reactions that transform other molecules, and in interaction with the environment, they form the basis for all the body's functions.

With the help of biotechnology, we have taken this development one step further. DNA sequences can be analyzed and stored on computers. The entire human genome, and the genomes of many other species, are today freely available on the internet. We can download different sequences, re-create them in laboratories, and insert them into new organisms. Genes are no longer copied only by DNA molecules. They are copied digitally, thereby illustrating how information can be transferred between different media—from one type of replicator to another.

Information is copied and mutated and thereby evolves by

means of natural selection. What Charles Darwin discovered in the middle of the 19th century was not simply the explanation for the origin of the species. He knew nothing about genes, epigenes, or memes. Nevertheless, he discovered the principle by which information arises, evolves, and forms the basis of life.[21] If it were presented today, we might have called it Darwin's theory of information.

INFORMATION IN CONCERT

So, what do theories about entropy, information, and memes have to do with cancer? The connection is closer than it may seem. As we have thoroughly discussed, cancer is about more than just genes, cells, and biology. It is also very much about ideas, emotions, and culture, and an integrated understanding of information provides an opportunity to see these two dimensions in context.

Let us take a fresh look at the cultural phenomenon of Shaman Durek and his allegedly supernatural abilities. "We [the shamans] can rotate the nucleus of the atoms, as well as the electrons in the atoms, which literally reduce age," he says in one of his many talk show interviews.[22] He provides neither evidence nor an explanation as to how this should be possible, and of course, everything is just his own fiction. I, therefore, challenge the self-proclaimed shaman to a duel between his supernatural and my natural abilities.

I can control genes in the body of people on the other side of the planet. I can affect all the cells in their body, perhaps for the rest of their lives. I can even influence the development of unborn children simply by the power of my mind. It may sound incredible, but these are abilities that we all have, and it is all scientifically sound and documented.

Let us say that an Australian friend of mine is visiting Norway to experience the beautiful Nordic winter. The sun is shining, and we have some fabulous days in the ski resort. Then suddenly, everything goes horribly wrong. By mistake, he ends up on the steepest, black diamond–marked slope. He loses control and crashes into a tree. The result is the worst imaginable. He is already dead when the helicopter arrives, and after a talk with the doctor, we conclude that I should convey the tragic message to my friend's pregnant wife. I call Australia and make sure she is not alone. Then I tell her what has happened. My words are transformed into electronic signals transmitted around the globe by radio waves and fiber-optic cables. In a fraction of a second, they are converted into sound waves by a mobile phone. These are perceived by the woman on the other side of the planet, and the effect is heartbreaking. She has a complete breakdown, not only mentally but also physically. Her whole body trembles, and she collapses inconsolably onto the floor.

A small story, a meme that originated in the Norwegian mountains, can create strong reactions in the body of a person in Australia. It may sound like magic, but it happens every day, and the various steps of the process are known in great detail. It is about the whole spectrum of science, from quantum physics and informatics to biology, psychology, and linguistics. Information is transferred from one medium to another. A few words, a pattern of nerve signals and sound waves, fit with existing patterns in someone's brain and activate a chain reaction. The electrical and chemical signals in the nerve cells lead to the release of hormones and other signaling molecules, which directly and indirectly affect the entire body.

Such stress responses may be transient, for example when we watch a scary movie. The level of stress hormones increases but usually returns to normal when the movie is over. Highly traumatic experiences, however, may cause lasting changes. War traumas or the loss of a family member affect not only people's minds but also their cells and organs. Mental stress activates biochemical signaling pathways that lead to changes in DNA methylation, which may turn specific genes on or off. This epigenetic mutation is then copied from one cell to the next, and a traumatic experience can literally remain in the body for the rest of our lives.[23]

A fetus, where the epigenes are rapidly evolving, is particularly susceptible. A mother's mental health, alcohol addiction, or eating habits may have a lasting impact. Studies show that epigenetic changes during fetal development may affect the child's immune system, intelligence, or risk of obesity later in life. My fortunately hypothetical phone call may thus have shaped the health and personality of my friend's unborn child in a permanent manner.[24]

Information encoded as genes, epigenes, or memes can make us both sick and healthy. The brain and the rest of the body are connected. The signals and communication pathways are subject to much research, and many studies have analyzed how everyday stress, for example during exams, affects the communication between the different cells in the immune system.[25] An unpleasant thought or experience can trigger signals in the body's complex information systems and thereby influence how susceptible we are to various diseases. Mental stress is not necessarily the main cause of a bodily disease. But in combination with a genetic or environmental predisposition, a stressful meme may represent the additional factor—the last straw—that triggers a cascade of events that make us sick.

Information crisscrosses through the body, and it is not just our own cells that talk to each other. The communication also involves the bacteria in our guts, our so-called microbiome. We have more bacteria inside our intestines than there are cells in the body, and they also want to be part of the conversation. The bacterial genes have adapted to the human body, while the human genes have adapted to the bacteria. Communication goes both ways, and how the microbiome affects health and disease is one of today's hottest research topics.[26]

The network of replicators and information channels also continues beyond the individual organisms. Genes and memes—biology and culture—affect each other in intricate ways. They are inseparably united, and if we consider only one or the other, we get less than half the story. Trying to combine the two perspectives is challenging, but the link between cancer and smoking may serve as an illustrative example.

Tobacco smoke leads to lung cancer. The connection is primarily about chemistry, genetics, and biology, but the smoking habit is also very much a cultural phenomenon. It is one of the most contagious memes in society, actively spread by cunning advertisements. It infiltrates the youth culture and continues to spread due to peer pressure and other psychological mechanisms. When young smokers grow into adults, they become involuntary role models who transmit the habit to their children. Accordingly, children of smokers are more likely to become smokers than children of nonsmokers.[27] The cancer meme is inherited from parent to child, alongside their genes, and the two systems of inheritance are closely integrated.

The smoking habit is undoubtedly a cultural phenomenon. Yet, the smoking meme's extraordinary success is directly related to genetics. The nicotine in tobacco targets a specific family of genes, encoding the nicotine receptors. These are protein antennas involved in several of the body's information channels.[28] In particular, they are connected to the so-called reward system in the brain that gives us desires and motivations and governs our basic need for satisfaction. It may be the search for the love of our life, the urge for a bucket of chocolate ice cream late at night, or the feeling of excitement when playing online casinos. The smoking meme uses the nicotine receptor to hijack our brain and produce an intense urge to continue the harmful habit. Even though it results in cancer and many other diseases, on average shortening life by about a decade, the selfish smoking meme thus continues to spread in the population.

Without this gene-meme interaction, the smoking habit would probably never have emerged. It is an intricate relationship that reaches far beyond the individual smoke. When the smoking meme leads to cancer by manipulating our genes, it promotes the development of new memes. Anti-smoking laws, for example, are memes that have emerged and spread in the population. For many years, these memes were strongly suppressed by the smoking meme. The idea of banning smoking and tobacco advertising was ridiculed and sabotaged by nicotine addicts. Then, as the epidemic of lung cancer and other tobacco-related diseases spread in the population, so did the anti-smoking memes. Smoking gradually evolved from being a trendy, upper-class activity to becoming a stigmatizing, low-status habit. In summary, we have learned that the smoking meme leads to cancer via a complex interplay with genes. Cancer then activated the anti-smoking memes. And today, the smoking meme is close to extinction in some societies.[29]

As a result of this development, lung cancer has become one of the most stigmatizing cancer diagnoses. While breast cancer ranks high in the hierarchy of disease, lung cancer is at the lower end of the scale. It is typically not the type of diagnosis people share on social media, and some patients choose to say they have other types of cancer to avoid the social stigma. As we have already discussed, society often uses a moral and normative perspective on disease. Lung cancer is generally interpreted as self-inflicted. To smoke is perceived as "your own choice," and many patients struggle with guilt.[30]

An integrated evolutionary understanding of cancer puts this blaming game in a different light. Can we blame a teenager, imprinted with the smoking meme from both parents and advertising, for getting cancer later in life? Is it your own fault if you have genes that are extra susceptible to the stimulating effect of nicotine? Is it possible to "just quit" when both genes and memes are working in the opposite direction? And what about people's genetic susceptibility to cancer? There are daily smokers—not many, but some—who have lived on to become centenarians. And there are people who never touched a cigarette and still got lung cancer. So, where is the justice?

The problem gets more fundamental for every question we ask and points toward one of the most fundamental of all: Do we have a free will? Can we override our genetic and cultural history, or is that just an illusion to provide meaning to our otherwise meaningless lives? What we do know is that biology and culture are not two separate domains. Body and soul work together. To understand life, we must understand this connection. Information, in the form of genes, memes, and other replicators, comes together to make people and other incredible organisms. We are disposable vehicles for information that propagates through time.

LEVELS OF UNDERSTANDING

Real learning is when you "suddenly understand something you have understood all your life, in a new way," wrote author and Nobel Prize laureate Doris Lessing.[31] We have come a long way in our quest to understand cancer, and it is time for a little summary.

Pedagogy, the science of learning, talks about different levels of thinking—the levels of cognition.[32] It is often emphasized that students should not only be able to reproduce knowledge. They should also be able to understand it. Memorizing the multiplication table, historical dates, or physical formulas is useful but provides little understanding. To understand the world, we must learn to see information in context. We must ask critical questions about where the information comes from, why there are conflicting views, and how we can make different ideas and perspectives fit together. Most importantly, we should question our own interpretation of the world. Thereby we climb higher on the ladder of understanding.

So let us start at the bottom. The most primitive way to understand cancer is to see it as an enemy, as something that attacks us, a punishment from God, or just bad luck. When we feel threatened, this may be our natural response, but it provides little insight and understanding of what cancer really is. Instead, it promotes ignorance and alienation. Most of all, it generates fear. The war metaphors are highly efficient at mobilizing support, and the political War on Cancer is rooted in this primitive perspective.

The next level of understanding explains cancer in terms of its many causes. We get cancer from smoking, radiation, food, viruses, genes, pollution, and much more. This linear causality is useful in promoting cancer prevention. Since there is a distinct cause, we can avoid the disease. Moreover, this perspective assigns responsibility, often to the patient. That can motivate a healthier lifestyle and a safer working environment but also gives rise to guilt and shame. Although important, this perspective to cancer does not provide much understanding. The list of different causes is almost inexhaustible. We seem to get cancer from everything, and there is no logic or meaning to the disease.

The next level of understanding concerns the mechanisms that lead to cancer. That is how cancer research is often communicated to the general public. The short explanation is that cancer is caused by mutations that make the cells run wild. It is about faulty control mechanisms, and the disease appears to be a technical problem. Accordingly, there should also be a technical solution. If only we can find a medicine that attacks the right molecules, turns on or off the crucial mechanisms, and kills the cancer cells more effectively, we can solve the problem. This perspective provides important insight into how genes and cells work, but the level of understanding remains limited. The mechanistic view makes it difficult to see the bigger picture, and the solution is always around the next corner.

A higher step on the ladder of understanding is to see cancer as a developmental process. Cancer consists of living cells that must be understood in the light of evolution. Mutations are not just faults in the machinery. They develop by natural selection in interaction with the environment. From this model, we can understand how cancer cells arise and develop inside the body, evade the immune system, and become resistant to therapy. Cancer cells are evolving, similar to viruses and bacteria, and the body is an ecological system.

We are approaching the top of the ladder, and the next step is to see the evolution of cancer from a larger biological perspective. Cancer development is not just about evolution inside the body. It is also related to the evolution of the species. It involves natural selection of genes and epigenes in their given environment, and the challenge is to see germline and somatic development in combination. Cancer is a consequence of how the body is organized—as a temporary cell colony developed by the genes to pass them on to the next generation. We are flowers that eventually wither and die.

The final step on the ladder, at least as far as we get in this book, is to see cancer in the light of an expanded understanding of evolution. Evolution and cancer are not just a matter of biology. Body and soul are connected. Genes, epigenes, and memes interact in a network of information. The complexity is perplexing, but the principle of evolution is simple. Life, or more precisely information, evolves by means of natural selection. In this perspective, cancer raises fundamental questions about what and who we are. What does it mean to be human, and where are cancer research and the biotechnological revolution taking us?

CHAPTER 9

The Solution

FALSE SOLUTIONS

We have reached the last chapter. Based on everything we have discussed so far, it is time to ask the big question: What is the solution to the problem? How do we make a world without cancer, and what will this world look like? Let us start by addressing some existing theories and beliefs.

On a spring day in the late 1970s, I discovered an elderly couple breaking branches off a tree on the edge of our family's garden. They were peering anxiously around as they stuffed twigs and leaves into a large black plastic bag. When they realized they had been discovered, they ran away like thieves, and I stood bewildered behind, looking at the wounded tree.

Later, I learned that the frightened couple was looking for

a miracle cure, which happened to be growing in our garden. Drinking ash tea, or decoction, was the new trend. It was supposed to cure everything from cancer and heart failure to diabetes and hemorrhoids. The demand was enormous, and seemingly ordinary people were climbing fences and committing petty crimes to get a piece of the magic tree.[1]

Stories about the healing powers of the ash tree can be traced far back in history. Both Greek and Norse mythologies describe ash as a life-giving force, and ash decoction is an established remedy in folk medicine.[2] How the Norwegian craze started in the 1970s is somewhat unclear, but the many women's magazines at the time had an important role. There you could read about one miraculous healing after another, and the publications had no interest in including critical voices.

I do not know what our two elderly ash thieves were seeking to heal, but I hope the stolen branches came to good use. Unfortunately, the effect cannot have been too convincing. The peculiar health trend soon faded, and today hardly anyone talks about ash decoction.

Now there are new miracle cures on the market. A popular one is turmeric, a plant in the ginger family that is eagerly promoted as a natural cure for cancer.[3] The orange spice used in Indian curry contains a substance called *curcumin*. This hormone-like molecule has been shown to inhibit the growth of some types of cancer cells in laboratory and animal experiments. Clinical trials suggest that curcumin also has some effect on cancer development in real life, and the idea that an exotic spice can cure cancer has resonated well in the world of complementary medicine. But it is not a cure. The attention that turmeric has received is vastly disproportional to the actual evidence.[4] It is the new vogue, and it does not help that one of the leading experts in the field, a researcher at the prestigious MD Anderson Cancer Center, was caught for massive research fraud. He had fabricated the results in several scientific articles believed to substantiate the effect of curcumin and turmeric on cancer.[5]

Yet, neither research fraud nor lack of evidence has dampened the marketing of turmeric as a natural cancer cure. The website CURE, which presents itself as America's largest online magazine about cancer, writes that "turmeric has shown fantastic effects against cancer."[6] The healing effect is supposedly well-documented, and the main problem is that people are unaware of the secret cure. The underlying conspiracy theory is that the pharmaceutical industry withholds information about turmeric and other natural cancer cures because they fear the competition.

The combination of actual research, undocumented claims, and conspiracy theories is typical of false cancer cures. There are numerous examples, but the promotion of low-carb diets is arguably the most important. The internet is flooded with articles and books on how cancer can be prevented and cured by avoiding carbohydrates. The aim is a so-called ketogenic diet, omitting everything that contains grains, potatoes, beans, and all kinds of sugar. The fewer carbohydrates, the better.

Many websites promote a ketogenic diet as the natural way to prevent and cure cancer.[7] The authors argue that the lack of carbohydrates starves cancer cells to death. We are told that this is how our Stone Age ancestors lived and that they almost never got cancer. If we go a little deeper, we also find conspiracy theories about researchers and health authorities that deny this revolutionary knowledge and deliberately mislead the general public.

Imagine if the solution to cancer had been that simple. Imagine if we could get rid of all cancer just by eating more like our ancestors. Unfortunately, that is not the case. Ancient people certainly got less cancer than we do, but that was primarily due to their limited life spans. They generally died of other causes before they got cancer. Yet, archaeological remains show that they got the same forms of cancer that we get.[8] Whether or not people of similar age got more or less cancer than we do today is pure speculation. For obvious reasons, we do not have statistics on the prevalence of cancer from the Paleolithic period.

Moreover, it is unclear whether the Paleolithic diet was all that healthy when we compare it to our standard of living. Healthy eating is defined primarily by its effect on longevity. Today we live longer than ever, and the average life expectancy in many economically developed countries is more than 80 years. Our prehistoric relatives were lucky if they survived puberty, and they did not have the luxury of being picky about food. In periods of food shortage, they ate what was available, often at risk of both malnutrition and food poisoning. The prospect of developing cancer in their seventies or eighties was the least of their problems. In the evolutionary perspective, dying from cancer would have been only a weak selection factor, unlikely to have influenced the development of either genes or eating habits.

It is also questionable if the Paleolithic diet was as low on carbohydrates as the proponents claim. Archaeological evidence indicates that cooking and frying plant foods to release carbohydrates was an important factor in human evolution.[9] Researchers have analyzed DNA from fossilized bacteria on the teeth of fossil humans and Neanderthals. They found that these bacteria had genes for metabolizing carbohydrates, just like bacteria in modern humans. Since the bacteria in their mouths lived off carbohydrates, we may thus assume that our Stone Age relatives did the same.[10]

The link between cancer and carbohydrates is generally complicated. The proponents of low-carb diets often reference the so-called Warburg effect, named after the German doctor and Nobel Prize winner Otto Heinrich Warburg.[11] The Warburg effect is the observation that cancer cells use glucose as energy to a greater extent than normal cells. This phenomenon is well-known in modern medicine and is explicitly applied to detect hidden tumors in the body. During a PET scanning, the patient gets a small dose of radioactive glucose injected into the bloodstream. Since the cancer cells absorb more glucose than other cells, they also become more radioactive. When the PET scanner measures radioactivity in the body, the cancer cells light up as bright dots on the computer screen. Thereby, even small tumors can be identified.[12]

Since cancer cells burn more glucose than normal cells, and glucose comes from carbohydrates, it seems reasonable to conclude that a diet low in carbohydrates will starve the cancer and prevent it from growing. Unfortunately, it is not that simple. As we have already established, cancer development is an evolutionary process. New mutations are emerging, and the cells best adapted to their environment multiply the fastest. To achieve that, they need extra energy, and it is no surprise that cancer cells evolve an increased ability to absorb and burn glucose. Many mutations related to cancer development are involved in energy metabolism, and there is a growing interest in this field of research.

Yet, there is no reason to believe that you can cure yourself of cancer by quitting carbohydrates.[13] If there is anything cancer research has shown us, it is that cancer cells are incredibly adaptable. We can irradiate them, poison them, or attempt to starve them, but much too often, some cells still survive and continue to multiply. Even if we manage to kill them all and cure that specific cancer, the problem remains. The older we get, the more likely we are to get another cancer. We are temporary cell colonies, and no diet can change this basic fact of life.

That does not mean that what we eat is irrelevant. As we have already discussed, a healthy diet prevents cancer. It also is essential for coping with and recovering from an arduous cancer treatment. But there are no quick fixes or miracle cures. For patients who are sick and nauseous from disease and medications, eating something you like is often more important than striving for the "perfect" diet. It is not just the cancer cells that need energy. It is hardly a good idea for patients to start an extreme diet that can drive them into malnutrition. Most importantly, cancer patients should consult their doctor to ensure that the diet they choose does not interfere with the treatment.

Patients with different cancer diagnoses have different dietary needs, but the basic principles apply.[14] Coarse grain products, beans, fruits, and vegetables are healthy, regardless of how the low-carb industry tries to paint carbohydrates as poison. On the other hand, there is total agreement among nutritional experts that we should avoid foods with added sugar and so-called fast carbohydrates.

Sweets, cakes, ice cream, white rice and pasta, and most importantly sugar sodas are not healthy. These foods provide a lot of energy while providing few other essential nutrients.

It is also worth noting that it was not the low-carb movement that discovered that sugar is bad for us. Health authorities, nutritionists, doctors, dentists, and school nurses have been trying to communicate this message for decades. The problem with the fake health prophets is that they always have to have a gimmick—an extreme idea that provides the attention they need to sell speculative books, deceptive courses, and overpriced food products.

The national and international dietary guidelines developed by large consortiums of experts are not very exciting. Yet they are by far the best guarantee we have for living as long as possible.[15] Therapies and diets that promise to miraculously cure cancer and other diseases are much more exciting, and many people are seduced by deceptive advertising. Recognizing the bluff may be challenging when actual research and scientific concepts are mixed with superstition and subtle conspiracy theories. Still, when something sounds too good to be true, it usually is.

NATURE'S SOLUTIONS

Claims that particular diets can cure cancer are often combined with stories about animals that never get the disease. These tales may involve everything from sharks and blue whales to elephants and naked mole rats. The truth, however, is that all these animals get cancer if they live long enough. Even insects can develop cancer-like tumors. Yet, most animals die of other causes long before they grow old and get cancer. That was also the case for humans before the age of modern medicine and our protected lifestyle. Similarly, animals that are kept artificially alive, like in a zoo, get cancer with increasing age, exactly like we do.[16]

Cancer development is related to age, and a species' tendency to get cancer should be seen in the context of its age of reproduction and life expectancy. Some animals live very long and get cancer later than others. The Galapagos turtles can be close to 200 years old as they move slowly around on their Pacific island.[17] Another example is the Greenland shark, which swims stealthily through the Arctic Sea while preying on sleeping seals. The oldest known specimen was estimated to be about 400 years old.[18]

So how is it possible to live so long without getting cancer? The one thing the Galapagos turtles and the Greenland sharks have in common is that they live slowly, both on the inside and the outside. Galapagos turtles have a resting heart rate of six beats per minute,[19] while the Greenland shark swims through the icy waters no faster than 2.6 kilometers per hour.[20] Everything about these animals is slow, including their metabolism and rate of cell division. The fact that they are also slow at getting cancer, therefore, makes perfect sense. In comparison, mice have a heart rate of up to 700 beats per minute and a lightning-fast metabolism.[21] They rush through life and rarely live longer than a couple years. If they do get older, for example in the protected environment of a laboratory, they soon get cancer.

Another species that has received much attention because it allegedly does not get cancer is the naked mole rat.[22] These peculiar-looking animals live in underground tunnels in the Horn of Africa and have exceptional longevity. While ordinary rats rarely get older than two to three years, the naked mole rat can become more than 30 years old. This extended life span has sparked a strong interest, and researchers are investigating why the naked mole rats do not age and get cancer as quickly as other rodents.

The answer is in the genes. These animals have a unique physiology, with more vigilant DNA repair and cellular control mechanisms than related species—including a more active TP53. Importantly, however, these genetic adaptations are also related to an exceptional lifestyle in a particular environment. The naked mole rats have evolved the ability to survive in an almost dormant state in underground tunnels with a minimum of oxygen. There, the nearly blind rats live in families organized somewhat similarly to ant colonies. Each colony consists of a queen, who mainly lies at rest and produces offspring with a few selected males. The rest of the family are sterile workers willing to sacrifice their lives to protect the colony. They build tunnels, gather food, and fight off snakes. Accordingly, they live significantly shorter lives than the queen and her lovers do.[23]

Like the Galapagos turtle and the Greenland shark, the naked mole rat demonstrates how a slow and protected lifestyle involves fewer cell divisions, fewer mutations, and later cancer. Their degree of genetic stability is almost as high as that of humans and fits well with the fact that naked mole rats can live almost as long as us before they get cancer or die of other causes.

Whether it is better to live fast and short or slow and long depends on the species' position in the ecosystem. Through natural selection, evolution finds the right balance in the given environment.[24] If the environment changes, however, the balance may be disrupted. *Homo sapiens* adapted to an environment where our life span was limited by bacterial infections, injury, and food shortage. Today, these external factors are largely eliminated. Instead, we have reached a level of longevity where internal factors—genetic instability and shortening telomeres—limit the length of our lives.

In theory, aging and cancer development can be delayed by slowing everything down. In principle, we can put the whole problem on ice, and there is an entire industry that does just that. So-called cryopreservation or cryonics aims to cheat death by freezing the body before it starts to decompose. Like religion, cryonics promises an afterlife, not in heaven but in a utopian future. The idea is to be revived in a more advanced society, and if you plan well and pay up, you may also be reunited with your family.[25]

There are many theories and opinions on how to eliminate cancer, and like cryonics, many are more related to religion than science. The basic premise remains. Cancer development is a consequence of how our body is made. While the genes in the germline are passed on from one generation to the next, the somatic line branches off and makes all the cells in the body. This is how we, and all other vertebrate animals, are made. But could it be any different? Is there another way to organize a multicellular organism? Indeed, there is.

Trees are organized fundamentally differently than animals. They do not have centralized and specialized organs such as the brain, heart, or intestines. Trees have basically the same structure repeated in the root, the stem, and the branches. They continue to grow throughout their lives, and the vital leaves responsible for photosynthesis are constantly renewed all over the "body."

This ability to diversify and rejuvenate is a property of the plant's growth zone. The so-called *meristem* contains stem cells that can develop into all the different types of plant cells—as opposed to our stem cells, which are more specialized. That is why it is possible to cut off a small twig, put it in water, and grow a completely new tree.[26]

Most importantly, the germ cells of trees do not come from a separate cell line. Nor is there a definite distinction between germinal and somatic development, which is a fundamental property of all vertebrate animals. Instead, germ cells develop in flowers and catkins that pop up in many different locations throughout the life of the organism. There is no separate evolutionary path for the genes to propogate to the next generation. And there are no somatic cells that will break free from the collaboration and become cancer cells.

Trees develop lumps and growths in response to injury and infections but do not develop cancer the way animals do. This difference is also reflected in the genes. Trees do not have a guardian of the genome, like our TP53, and there is generally less control of DNA damage and cell division. To explore this difference, some researchers transferred the human TP53 gene to a plant, and the result was interesting. The guardian of the genome interfered with the plant's control mechanisms, and the gene-manipulated organisms appeared to age faster than normal plants.[27]

Since trees do not have a problem with the cells running wild, they do not need the telomeres to keep track of the number of cell divisions.[28] Instead, the length of their telomeres is maintained throughout life, and the cells can continue to divide indefinitely. Whereas we die of aging and cancer, trees mainly die from external influences such as injuries, infections, or droughts. If the conditions are right, some species can live almost forever. The oldest individual trees are about 5,000 years old, but there are so-called clonal trees that have lived for more than 10,000 years.[29] These are trees that constantly grow new sprouts from their underground root system. Accordingly, it is not the visual trees that keep on living but an underground organism that continues to make new trees.

In conclusion, trees demonstrate a principal solution to cancer. They are organized completely differently from animals and highlight how cancer is related to the separation of the germinal and the somatic cell lines. Importantly, however, it is this fundamental property that defines us as animals—and humans.

IMMUNOLOGICAL WARFARE

In recent years, the biggest headlines about breakthroughs in cancer research have been related to immunotherapy, and many seem to think that activating the immune system is the solution to cancer. For the sake of clarity, we are not talking about the complementary therapy version of "activating the immune system," which adds little beyond the general advice of healthy living. We are talking about the result of groundbreaking, meticulous research about the genes and cells that control the body's defense against external enemies. That is where we started, with the newspaper article about Gustav Gaudernack's pioneering research on cancer vaccines.[30] So, let us explore what the sensational headlines are all about.

Immunotherapy uses biotechnology to activate the body's defense system to find and kill cancer cells. To understand how this works, we need to know a little more about the immune system. Noticeably, we are now unavoidably going to use a lot of war metaphors, which many have criticized for giving a misleading understanding of cancer. Used with deliberation, however, metaphors can be both relevant and helpful.

Our bodies are literally at war—at least if we define war as a battle to fend off intruders and stay alive.[31] Various microorganisms, known as viruses, bacteria, fungi, amoebas, and other parasites, constantly try to invade us. Without a solid defense and the ability to strike back, we would quickly be overwhelmed and die. This essential function is clearly demonstrated by people who, for some reason, have a compromised immune system. Even a small skin infection or a common cold may run out of control.

Our genes have thus evolved a complex system to recognize and eliminate all types of microorganisms, and the immune system has many similarities to an actual military organization. It is divided into different branches with different responsibilities. That includes a border patrol, an intelligence service, and a cavalry that quickly comes to the rescue. As we shall see, the immune system even has a military academy for training officers.

To understand how this defense works without having to become a full-time immunologist, we should focus on the basic principles. The key is, as always, to see biology in the light of evolution. Like everything else in the body, the immune system is made up of cells controlled by genes and epigenes. And one type of cells—the T cells—are especially critical. These cells function like security police. They circulate between the blood and the lymphatic system and stop other cells at random. They ask for identification papers, conduct a body search, and if things are not in order, they execute the target on the spot.

The immune system is, in many aspects, an authoritarian surveillance system, and the other cells are genetically programmed to comply. This surveillance is essential for survival but also dangerous, especially if it gets out of control. When T cells attack the body's normal cells by mistake, it leads to so-called autoimmune diseases, including potentially life-threatening conditions like rheumatoid arthritis, psoriasis, and type 1 diabetes. Accordingly, there are several control mechanisms to avoid such self-inflicted damage.

Every cell in the body has a system for displaying pieces of its internal proteins on the surface so that the T cells can inspect them. Since the sequences of the proteins are encoded in DNA, this surveillance system is in indirect control of the genes. The T cells check that the cells in the body have the right genes, and if something does not match, they attack.

So, how can the T cells know the difference between all the body's own proteins and those of a myriad intruding bacteria and viruses? Again, evolution is the key. Specific genes in the T cells are rearranged in a similar manner to the antibody genes in the B cells. Each T cell thereby develops a unique antenna—or receptor—that can recognize a specific piece of protein, which the other cells may or may not display on the surface.

At the outset, there are thus T cells that can recognize and attack all types of proteins, including those of our own normal cells. Before the T cells can be deployed to service, they must thus be trained. This training occurs in a small, inconspicuous gland just below the sternum. The thymus, from which the T cells get their T, is the body's military academy.[32] Here the T cell recruits undergo a harsh selection process. The cells that recognize the body's own proteins are told to commit suicide and are eliminated by apoptosis. Accordingly, the cells that graduate from the thymus should recognize only foreign proteins made by foreign genes. These elite officers, which can distinguish self from non-self, then become commanders of the other cells of the immune system.

The T cell's system for "body-searching" all the other cells of the organism is essential for detecting and eliminating viruses that inject themselves into our cells. T cells that recognize virus-infected cells are then stimulated to multiply and are stored in the body in the event of a new infection with the same virus. The system learns by means of natural selection, and we become immune.

As T cells are able to recognize changes within other cells, they can, in principle, also detect and eliminate mutated cancer cells. And that is precisely what Gustav Gaudernack had realized when I first met him in the early 1990s. His hypothesis was as follows: If we can show that T cells recognize specific mutations in the cancer cells, we can also create a vaccine that stimulates these T cells to attack the cancer.[33]

Gustav was setting up a research group to explore this theory, and while other colleagues were studying the T cells, my task was to identify the target mutations in the cancer cells.[34] It was a meticulous endeavor, but after a few years of intense research, we could confirm the hypothesis. The T cells could indeed recognize and attack cancer cells comprising the specific mutations—not only in the laboratory but also in the bodies of actual cancer patients.

Gustav's other brilliant idea was to patent the mutated protein as a vaccine. There were several alternative candidates. The first to be tested were mutations in the previously mentioned K-RAS gene, and the results were promising. The most exciting results, however, came from a vaccine concerning the telomeres.[35] As we already discussed, these repeated DNA sequences sit at the end of the chromosomes and are counting down to the day the cells become old and die by apoptosis. The cancer cells, on the other hand, have activated a gene that extends the telomeres. That stops the countdown, and the cells can live forever.

This gene makes a protein called *telomerase* and is normally activated in the early stages of embryological development. Then, when the telomeres are established, it is turned off. If telomerase is reactivated later in life, it is thus a sign of cancer. The gene is, in fact, activated in almost all cancer cells, and the telomerase protein is a unique target for immunotherapy. A vaccine that contains pieces of this protein can, in principle, activate T cells to kill almost any type of cancer cells, and that is why it has been labeled a "universal cancer vaccine."[36]

However, while immunotherapy and cancer vaccines represent an exceptional scientific breakthrough, there are also many challenges. The first problem is getting the T cells to attack the cancer cells. Although cancer cells have many mutations, they are also very similar to normal cells. In particular, they transmit signals that inhibit the T cells from attacking. A major challenge in immunotherapy was therefore to find a way to prevent this inhibition signal. The solution is a type of medicine that blocks the receiving antenna on the T cells. Thereby, they attack the cancer cells even though they are camouflaged. The drugs are known as checkpoint inhibitors, and in 2018, immunologists Tasuku Honjo and James Allison received the Nobel Prize for this discovery.[37]

A key strategy in today's immunotherapy is to combine cancer vaccines with checkpoint inhibitors. The vaccine stimulates the right T cells, while the checkpoint inhibitors remove the barriers to attack. It is almost like training Navy SEALs and then dropping them off in parachutes behind enemy lines. The method seems most effective against cancers with many mutations, like lung cancer. The results are promising, and in some cases, the patients become completely cancer-free.

Yet, starting a war within the body is not without risk. Blocking the signals that prevent the T cells from attacking other cells also increases the risk of autoimmune reactions. Immunotherapy may lead to inflammation in various organs, and doctors must be careful not to overstimulate the immune system. Even though the treatment is more gentle than chemotherapy, it is not without side effects, and we still know little about the long-term consequences.[38]

Another problem is related to the evolution of cancer. Like bacteria and viruses, cancer cells evolve and may become resistant to whatever we use to kill them. That also applies to immunotherapy. Natural selection favors mutations and epimutations that evade T cell surveillance and attacks. Although the T cells evolve by natural selection to get better weapons, they do not always win the battle. The situation is similar to an arms race where you always have to evolve and adapt to keep the advantage.

In evolutionary biology, researchers talk about the *red queen effect* when describing such races. The term is a reference to one of Lewis Carroll's stories about Alice in Wonderland. In the book *Through the Looking-Glass,* Alice comes to the land of the Red Queen and discovers something curious. She is running at full speed. Yet she is getting nowhere. Alice wonders what is going on, and the Red Queen explains, "Now, here, you see, it takes all the running you can do, to keep in the same place. If you want to get somewhere else, you must run at least twice as fast as that!"[39]

A classic red queen effect is the continuous race between prey and predator, for example, cheetahs and antelopes. Both species are selected for their ability to run fast, thereby becoming better at hunting and fleeing. In relation to each other, however, they are standing still. We see the same effect with regard to our own enemies. A few decades ago, many believed that the discovery of antibiotics was the end to bacterial infections. Today, we know that the more antibiotics we use, the more tenacious bacteria we get. The microorganisms are adapting to our defense, and so-called multiresistant bacteria are on the rise worldwide. Whether it is antibiotic-resistant bacteria, new virus variants, or cancer cells, we must keep running.

Another challenge with immunotherapy is the aging of the immune system. Like other cells in the body, T cells and B cells accumulate mutations and get older. They become weaker and less coordinated. If they do not die of old age, they also will evolve into uncontrollable cancer cells. Accordingly, the efficiency of immunotherapy weakens as we get older.

That brings us to the last and most fundamental reason why not even immunotherapy is the solution to cancer. Cancer treatment, whether it is radiation therapy, chemotherapy, surgery, or immunotherapy, is basically about killing cancer cells. Thereby we cure cancer one case at a time. Another year, a couple of months, or maybe just a few weeks to live can mean a lot to the individual patient and their relatives. Yet, killing cancer cells does not solve the problem that cancer increases with age. The longer we live, the more cancer there will be in the population. The fundamental problem is aging. All our cells are gradually accumulating mutations. We can slow down this process by living as healthily as possible, but with every cell division, there will be errors in the copying of genes and epigenes. If we really want to cure cancer, we thus have to cure aging.

THE IMMORTAL BODY

The fundamental problem is that all the cells in our body are slowly but surely evolving toward cancer. If we just continue to kill cancer cells, we will, sooner or later, end up killing ourselves. At some point, the treatment becomes more lethal than the disease itself, and it is better to let it be. That is also how it works in clinical practice. Doctors must often convey the difficult message that the treatment is no longer effective and should focus on improving the quality of life rather than extending it.[40]

The fundamental problem remains. We are temporary cell colonies that the genes have made to get to the next generation. We are not made to live as long as possible. To cure cancer "once and for all," we must come up with something more radical than killing cancer cells. We must find a way to rejuvenate the body.

In principle, we can replace our old cells and organs with new ones as they get old and unstable. That may sound like science fiction, but it is, to some extent, already a reality. Some types of blood and lymphatic cancers are routinely treated by replacing old cells with new ones. Healthy stem cells can be harvested from the bone marrow of a young and healthy blood donor or carefully extracted from the patient's blood. The next step is to kill off all the old blood cells with cytotoxic drugs, thereby removing the cancer cells, as well as the normal blood cells. The blood system gets a clean start before the healthy stem cells are inserted.[41] These cells will then keep multiplying. They give rise to all the different types of cells in the blood, and if everything goes according to plan, the patient is cured.

Stem cell transplantation is especially suited for leukemia and other blood-related diseases since the cells can be easily retrieved and inserted through a blood vessel. From there, they find their way to where they are needed. For other organs, it is more complicated. In principle, however, all types of cancer can be treated by removing old cells and transplanting new ones.

In some cases of liver cancer, the tumor may be too difficult to remove, or the whole organ may malfunction.[42] Instead of treating the cancer, it is thus better to replace the liver with a healthy and cancer-free organ. The new organ may be obtained from a person who has died, for example in a traffic accident, but access to new body parts is obviously a limiting factor for such treatments. The organ must also be intact and transplanted from the donor to the recipient within hours. Most importantly, it must be compatible with patient's tissue type.[43]

To overcome these limitations, many researchers are exploring new ways to grow cells and organs. One approach is to use pigs as organ donors. Pigs are biologically very similar to humans and are already bred on a large scale for food production. Genetically manipulated pigs, with human tissue types, may thus provide an inexhaustible source of new organs, and the results are promising. The first heart transplantation from pig to human was performed in 2022, and the patient lived for two months.[44]

Some will say that it is unethical to breed animals to make spare parts for humans. Others will argue that it is more unethical if we do not use this opportunity to save lives. Anyhow, the biggest obstacle to transplant organs from animals to humans is not animal ethics but the danger of transmitting infections. Designing pigs that are genetically similar to humans and then using them as organ donors entails a great risk of transmitting viruses from one species to another. In fact, the first patient, mentioned previously, likely died of a pig virus that had infected the transplanted organ.[45] With the swine flu and COVID-19 fresh in mind, starting a massive scheme to transplant organs between species is thus hardly a good idea.

The concept of curing cancer by replacing cells and body parts is nevertheless interesting, and it is intriguing to take the idea a step further. In theory, it is possible to replace the entire body, and there are more or less serious researchers who claim that they are in the process of developing such surgical procedures.[46] Whether the head gets a new body or the body gets a new head is a matter for debate. Yet, as our identity is first and foremost connected to the brain, it is probably most correct to call it a body transplant, not a head transplant. The head gets a new body, not the other way around.

Most experts would say that such procedures are both unrealistic and unethical, at least with current technology. Even if it is possible to connect the head and the body without killing the patients, they would be paralyzed from the neck down. Despite much research, no one has found a way to heal complete injuries to the spinal cord. Yet, it is not unthinkable that within a few decades, it will be possible to connect nerve pathways so that a head and a body can be fully reconnected. In principle, we will then be able to replace our aging, cancerous bodies with new and healthy ones. Another question is where these new bodies will come from and who should receive such treatment. Some people have to die young and healthy in order for others to live, and although a full-body transplant is an intriguing concept, it seems better suited for science fiction than real life.

Today's research front is not so much about traditional transplantation of organs from one person to another. The new research field is *regenerative medicine*, meaning various techniques for genetically manipulating, renewing, and replacing the cells in the body with biotechnology.[47] One increasingly common method is to renew the body with cells from our own childhood. That may sound like time travel, but it is actually not that complicated. You need only resourceful parents that start preparing for your old age the day you are born. Immediately after birth, blood is drawn from your umbilical cord and frozen in liquid nitrogen. These stem cells can then be used to renew your blood cells later in life, not just in case of cancer or other diseases, but as a general boost to your aging body. So, in order to be a good parent, in this modern age, it is increasingly common to "bank" newborn children's cord blood for the future.

Researchers are also getting better at mapping and controlling the epigenes. Soon they will be able to take umbilical cord stem cells and turn them into any type of cell in the body. This combination of stem cell research and gene manipulation is controversial. One thing is to grow cells that can cure a specific disease. But once we can control the stem cells and their epigenes, we control life. We will be able to make any type of organism, including humans, by design.

This technology has already been demonstrated. In 2008, the mouse Tiny was grown from skin stem cells taken from an adult mouse that had been frozen for 16 years.[48] And there is every reason to believe this technique will also work on humans. In principle, we can grow our own identical twins from our frozen stem cells. These cells can then give rise to all cell types, and since they are made from our own cells, the cultured organs will be perfectly compatible with our old bodies.

To design, or at least to select, an embryo in order to save somebody else is also already a reality. "Savior siblings" are children created by in vitro fertilization to be genetically compatible with a brother or sister who suffers a life-threatening genetic disease.[49] The prime example is children suffering from *thalassemia*, a deadly blood disease. These children can be saved by stem cell transplantations from a healthy person with the same tissue type. Yet, such a person can be very hard to find, and their best chance is to get a sibling with the right tissue type who has no thalassemia. Accordingly, the embryos must be genetically tested and carefully selected.

Such genetic design of babies is ethically controversial. Making a child to get spare parts for others challenges our fundamental value system. Some will argue it turns embryos and children into remedies and commodities instead of individual human beings who have their own rights and values. On the other hand, if having a child with a specific combination of genes can save a brother or sister from dying, it is also problematic not to take advantage of the new technology.

Who should decide why and how someone has a child, and how far are we willing to go to save a life?

This technological revolution has its own dynamics. Knowledge is power, and researchers, companies, and nations are competing to develop and take advantage of the new technology. Underneath, however, is an even stronger driving force—people's desire to live long and healthy lives. The ability to save or prolong lives has a tendency to trump everything else. When faced with a choice between saving human lives, especially children, or abstract concerns about ethics and long-term consequences, it is almost impossible not to choose life.

The expectations of what gene therapy and stem cell research can do for cancer treatment, especially in young patients, are one of the strongest drivers of biotechnology. The new technology opens up tremendous opportunities, and public opinion demands that governments do everything in their power so that we all can live as long as possible.

Powerful interest groups, like the Norwegian Cancer Society, complain that the gene therapy revolution is developing too slowly. And they have strong arguments: "With gene therapy, people who are about to become blind get their sight back. Children, who are immobile by muscular dystrophy, sit up. Cancer patients, who have been sentenced to death, become cancer-free."[50] How can anyone argue against that?

Childhood cancer is rare and increasingly curable. Yet, every case is heartbreaking, and it is easy to agree that we should do everything in our power to prevent children from suffering. Gene therapy and stem cell treatment may, at least in theory, eliminate cancer in the younger age groups. It is thus tempting to cheer for faster development, but where are these demands and expectations taking us? We are not just curing a disease; we are also opening the door to a technology that will change life and society forever. It will change how people are made and what it means to be human.

We should also note that the big demand and market for cancer therapy is not primarily about children. Cancer development is first and foremost a consequence of the natural aging process. The better we become at treating cancer and other diseases, the longer we live and the more cancer there will be in the population. The growing cancer epidemic is not a problem modern medicine is about to solve. Like so many other societal problems, it is a result of our technological development.

It is this problem that we are now trying to solve with even more advanced technology. Life is no longer a magical mystery. It has become hard science and big business, and many of the world's most influential people and companies are turning their resources toward the biotech industry. Leaders of major companies such as Google and Facebook are investing heavily in regenerative medicine, and the goal is nothing less than to cure death.[51] Jeff Bezos, the founder and chairman of Amazon, recently invested billions of dollars in antiaging research.[52] And he is only the latest among the many tycoons now seeking the holy grail of immortality.

Whether the billionaires really aim to live forever or just see the research as a good investment is somewhat unclear. Larry Ellison, however, another super-billionaire, has stated his view quite bluntly: "Death has never made sense to me," he says in an interview.[53] That is undoubtedly a relatable sentiment to many. In the depth of sorrow and grief, death seems meaningless. Yet, the idea of defeating death itself seems rather absurd to most of us, and it would be interesting to know how Mr. Ellison envisions a world where nobody dies.

A few years ago, I attended an international research conference about cancer and aging that may give us some clues. The head of a large center for antiaging research enthusiastically explained what he hoped to achieve. He was confident that within a few decades, it would be possible to live to be at least 200 years old. Intrigued and worried, I asked him a question: "If we stop dying, there will be no room for new people. The planet is already overpopulated, and a world without death implies a world without children. What do you think about that?" His answer was as short as it was revealing: "Not my table!" Then he added, "I am just a researcher and only interested in the science. But look at China. They have done it." He was apparently referring to how China's one-child policy has actively contributed to the low birth rate in the country. It was a chilling remark, and the prestigious research leader provided no ethical concerns about the technological and societal disruption he was actively promoting.

Do we really want a world without children, where the same people keep living while replacing their old body parts? I expect that Larry Ellison, Jeff Bezos, and the other billionaires have already thought of this problem and may have a plan of their own. Curing death will surely not be cheap, and the technology will be available to only a very few privileged people. Even today, the rich have a considerable advantage. In the United States, the wealthiest 1% of the population live significantly longer than the poorest percentage—about ten years for women and fifteen years for men.[54] At the global scale, the inequality of life expectancy and general health is enormous, and we see the contours of a world where the rich can buy eternal life while the poor continue to die as early as before. Are we heading for a world ruled by immortal super-narcissists who do not see the value of children and whose only concern is their own money and power? The vision of the immortal body may not be as appealing as it first sounds.

Some researchers counter this argument by saying neither cancer research nor regenerative medicine is about curing death. The goal we are striving for is that people can live healthy, meaningful lives without cancer and other diseases until they die happy and satisfied of old age. Let us say that this scenario is achievable. Assume that everybody lives healthily until 120 years of age and then dies quickly and painlessly. It sounds nice. But how realistic is it really? The longer we extend our lives, the more disease there will be in the population. Unfortunately, it is the last and not the first part of life that is extended.

Anyhow, let us assume that we are able to provide everybody with 120 years of good quality life. Will everybody then agree to die at this age? The basic problem is that people do not want to die. There will always be a will and a market for medication and procedures that make us live a little longer, even if our health is deteriorating. Most people will accept a life with a certain level of pain and illness if the alternative is death.

We may most certainly be able to extend life with the help of biotechnology, but the idea that we can create a society where everyone is healthy until they die suddenly of old age seems highly unrealistic. The only way to achieve this utopia would be in an authoritarian society where it is decided for us how long we are allowed to live. Someone or something has to determine when to turn off the switch, which will hardly happen without protests.

A more likely scenario is that we will continue to prolong life by all available means, even if it makes us increasingly more dependent on health care. The economic and psychological driving forces are unstoppable, and the immortal body may become a reality before we know it, at least for a selected few. Yet, we may want to listen to a super-billionaire who decided not to fight death. Steve Jobs, the legendary leader of Apple who died of a rare form of pancreatic cancer, said it like this: "No one wants to die. Even people who want to go to heaven don't want to die to get there. And yet death is the destination we all share. No one has ever escaped it. And that is as it should be, because Death is very likely the single best invention of Life. It is Life's change agent. It clears out the old to make way for the new. Right now the new is you, but someday not too long from now, you will gradually become the old and be cleared away. Sorry to be so dramatic, but it is quite true."[55]

"Memento mori" is a Latin meme that is as relevant today as it was thousands of years ago.[56] The phrase is repeated throughout our cultural history and can be recognized in music, literature, and arts. Even in the modern world of computer games, "memento mori" is a frequent theme. It means "remember death" or "remember that you are going to die" and functions as a note to ourselves that life is short. Death defines what it means to be human. It frames our lives, provides meaning and urgency, and creates space for new generations.

Yet, romantic speeches in defense of death are empty words to anyone afraid of dying. The pain of losing a loved one can be excruciating, and nothing is more painful than a child with a lethal disease. If given a choice, most of us would probably seize the chance to live as long as possible—at least as long as we are reasonably healthy.

Current knowledge suggests that it is possible to extend human lives significantly, and we will almost certainly take advantage of this technology, even if it involves fundamental disruption of society. We may be approaching a level of development where those who have the resources will be able to buy the extra years they need to stay alive and always be one step ahead of death. The billionaires are already lining up, as our generation may be the last where everybody dies.[57]

THE IMMORTAL SOUL

Even if regenerative medicine can renew the human body indefinitely, one problem remains. We can replace cells and body parts one by one, but we face a challenge when we get to the brain. The brain cells also accumulate genetic and epigenetic mutations with age. Similar to the other cells in the body, there are two alternative outcomes. The first option is that the control mechanisms step in and tell the cells to shut down. The brain withers, and we gradually acquire dementia due to Alzheimer's and other so-called neurodegenerative diseases. The second option is that the brain cells accumulate mutations that disengage the control mechanisms. They continue to divide, and natural selection drives the development of brain cancer.

In principle, we can grow new brain cells artificially in the same way as other cells, and there is a lot of research on how to use stem cells to treat age-related brain diseases.[58] Animal experiments show promising results, but there is one fundamental challenge. If we start tampering with the cells responsible for our memory and identity, we are literally in danger of losing our minds. The big question is thus, "Can we renew the brain and still be ourselves?"

That will not be easy. Our attitudes and opinions are, first and foremost, a result of our cultural heritage, encompassing everything we have learned and experienced. General personality traits, such as the tendency for aggression or depression or whether we are introverts or extroverts are, to some extent, encoded in our DNA. Yet, most of our thoughts, ideas, and behavior patterns do not come from genes but from memes we have collected. How these memes are stored in different parts of the brain is still unclear. But we know they are there, somehow encoded as molecular patterns and biochemical processes maintained and developed throughout life. Accordingly, if we are going to replace our brain with a new one, we also need to reprogram it. We must somehow transfer all our memes from the old brain to the new. Otherwise, we will wake up as somebody else, and then the whole point of eternal life will be gone.

Growing new brains and programming them with our old thoughts is far beyond today's knowledge and technology, but there may be a simpler solution. A major paradox in today's cancer research and biomedical development is that everything we do aims to heal the body. Still, it is not the body we seek to preserve. We are using enormous resources to maintain the life of our withering cells and organs, but what we really care about are the memes that make up our personality and consciousness. It is the soul that wants to live forever.

The body is a tool that the genes have developed to pass themselves on to the next generation. Thereby they have also developed
the brain as a medium for the soul. When the job is done, the body
dies and takes the brain and soul with it in the process. So, can we
imagine a world where the memes that make our soul can break
free from the body? That may sound like religion or creative science
fiction, but if we take a look around, that seems to be exactly what
is going on. Human history and today's technological development
are very much a story about the memes' struggle to free themselves
from the genes.[59]

The invention of language allowed memes to jump effortlessly
from one brain to another. Thereby, they could spread and evolve
throughout the population, regardless of the genes' path through
history. With the development of writing, they could be stored
on stone tablets and rolls of paper outside the perishable body.
The printing press made it possible to mass-produce large meme
complexes, such as the Bible and scientific dissertations, at an ever-
faster pace.

Some may argue that history is repeating itself and that the world
is not really going forward. There have been major setbacks in both
biological and cultural evolution. Yet, this fundamental aspect seems
to be highly persistent: The speed and fidelity of information pro-
cessing is always increasing. Evolution is about copying information
as efficiently as possible, and the process seems unstoppable.

Right now, we are experiencing a digital revolution where enormous amounts of information are produced and transmitted at the
speed of light, increasingly independent of both genes and brains.
Large computers receive, process, and convey information day and

night. They regulate the economy, air traffic, the power grid, and our news feeds. Humans still play an important role, but the argument that *we* are in control becomes weaker every day.

The digitalization of society has its own dynamics, and the history of the old-fashioned bank book is a good example. Not so many years ago, most people had a small book where the bank teller, with pen and paper, documented how much money each person had in their bank account. With the introduction of computers, this information was transferred to the digital world. There was an intermediate period where the bank printed bank statements that were sent to our physical mailboxes. Yet, with the development of the internet and mobile apps, everything reminiscent of the old bank book was gone. The information in the book still exists, and it is still physical. Digital codes in microprocessors, wires, optical fibers, wireless networks, hard drives, and monitors are as physical as everything else in the world. They exist as electromagnetic patterns, which are remarkably more efficient than pen and paper at transmitting information.

What happened to the bank book is also happening to many other objects. Brick-and-mortar shops are rapidly replaced by online retailers. Post offices, banks, and government bureaus are turning into internet portals. They are populated by computer programs rather than people. We got online health services, with or without live healthcare professionals, and everything got its own mobile app.

Today, when somebody plans to build a new factory, a ship, or an aircraft, they start by making a digital twin of the construction.[60] This twin is not just a construction plan but also a system that monitors and controls everything in the physical structure. It regulates access, climate, data security, production processes, and much more. These digital systems are then stored in giant databases that we can access and explore, for example, through Google Maps. There they will live on after the physical construction is gone, and every day an increasing number of new items are added to this digital twin world.

Even warfare has moved to the digital world. Nations, companies, and terrorist organizations are targeting each other with hacker attacks, fake news, and social media manipulation. They are fighting with computer codes rather than physical weapons, and according to national security agencies, the first cyber world war is already in full motion.[61]

Concurrently, the gaming and entertainment industry is developing an ever-larger universe of fantasy worlds where we can choose our own identities. We can communicate, compete, fight, and live in increasingly complex and life-like environments, and the distinction between the digital and the physical world is gradually disappearing.

Practically every aspect of human civilization is being transferred to the digital world.[62] So, what about human beings? We are also in the process of getting digital twins. Many of us already have smartwatches and mobile apps monitoring our physical activity, heart rate, blood pressure, blood sugar, sleep, and menstruation cycle. They tell us what to do and sound the alarm if something is wrong. Information from these apps can then be combined with all the information in our digital medical records, including blood tests, medical images, and prescription medication. Soon it will also contain all the genetic and epigenetic information that defines our biology.

Alongside this biomedical information, many of us are in the process of transferring all our cultural information to the digital domain. Every day, we eagerly upload new pieces of our identity to the social media platforms—at least the parts we want to show off. Our images, opinions, feelings, preferences, and positions are stored in the all-encompassing cloud of information. We have friends, followers, and people we follow, whom we know only digitally. Our online identities are, for many people, more important than the ones associated with their physical bodies.

Sooner or later, and perhaps before we know it, there will be more information about us in the *cloud* than in our brains. It will certainly be more accessible—even after we die. Facebook and other digital platforms also store information after our death. In a few decades, they will have more dead profiles than living people.[63] Our digital twins already contain more information than any of us have the capacity or knowledge to control. It thus seems as if what happened to the old bank book is about to happen to us. We are moving to the digital world, while our biological body gradually becomes more irrelevant.

How this new lifeform will evolve is difficult to predict. People of flesh and blood will probably be around for many more years, but their role will change. We see the contours of a society where biology and information technology combine to form something completely new. Sensors and devices connect our body and brain to the digital cloud, while increasingly more advanced technology manipulates genes, epigenes, and biological processes. All types of biological information are mapped, analyzed, and compiled in enormous databases, and life itself is getting a digital twin. The only thing missing is a logic that brings all the information about us together—a computer program or algorithm that continues to control our digital twin even after the body and brain have disintegrated. We need a little *artificial intelligence*—or *AI*.[64]

A few decades ago, it was considered almost unthinkable that a machine could be better than humans at solving complex cognitive tasks like playing chess. Today, even Magnus Carlsen, the five-time world champion, does not have a chance against the algorithms, and they keep surpassing us at increasingly more advanced functions.[65] There are still everyday tasks like car driving and putting the dishes in the dishwasher that humans do better than computers, but that is merely a matter of time. AI is already immensely better than the human brain at analyzing problems related to large amounts of data. Algorithms decide most of the trading on the stock market and make decisions in a matter of nanoseconds that may have profound implications for all of us. They have been developed to help us, but their goal is to build wealth and power, not the good of humankind.

Several people have tried to warn us about AI. According to the late physicist Stephen Hawking, "The development of full artificial intelligence could spell the end of the human race."[66] Having lived a life paralyzed by the degenerative neurological disease ALS, Hawking knew better than most what medical and technological advances could mean for a person. Bound to the wheelchair, he probably yearned for another body. As he lost the ability to speak and move, he became completely dependent on advanced technology to be able to both breathe and communicate with the outside world. Yet, or perhaps precisely because of that, Stephen Hawking warned us about the dangers of AI, as well as biotechnology.

Another person who knows better than most what AI is capable of is Elon Musk. The super-entrepreneur behind Tesla and SpaceX has also given us a harsh warning: "At least when there's an evil dictator, that human is going to die. But for an AI, there would be no death. It would live forever. And then you'd have an immortal dictator from which we can never escape."[67] Yet Musk is one of the major developers of AI. Tesla is a world leader in self-driving cars, and Musk is also the founder of Neuralink, a company that develops brain implants that connect directly to the digital world. Such technology will further erase the boundaries between biology and technology. Based on the slogan "If you cannot beat them, join them," Musk argues that it is better to take control of the technology than to be controlled by it.[68] For most of us, that is not so easy. Yet, it is probably our only option. We must try to understand what is going on, take control of our lives, and build the world we want. Elon Musk may not be a benevolent savior of our civilization, but when he says that AI should be subjected to international democratic regulations, we do wise to listen.

Some believe that the fear of AI is exaggerated. They argue that it is just another tool that may be used for good or evil, and it is up to us to use it wisely. "We know cancer is going to be cured," says Rich Kaplan, general manager of employee experience and human resources services at Microsoft.[69] A former CEO of Google Norway argues that "I am absolutely certain that the major medical challenges—cancer, Alzheimer's, Parkinson's, ALS—will not be solved by the medical research community, but by AI."[70]

They may be right, but probably not in the way they and many other people think. Their basic understanding is that AI will analyze the available information in new and innovative manners. Thereby, we can develop the ultimate treatment that lets people live long and cancer-free for the rest of their lives. That is an admirable goal, but the premise is based on the old, misguided notion that we can treat ourselves out of the cancer epidemic. As we have already clarified, this is a logical fallacy.

AI will not *find* the solution to cancer. It *is* the ultimate solution to cancer. The advantages of converting to digital life are evident. Our identity is liberated from the mortal body, and as long as no one erases us, we have eternal life. The soul is free, and billions of human bodies will no longer have to be fed and transported. Environmental and animal-unfriendly food production will be redundant. Our digital self will live on electrical energy, which we can get directly from solar power. If we want to conquer space, the planets we aim to habitat will need neither water nor oxygen. We need only a receiver at the other end. Then we can teleport ourselves wherever we want to go. It may sound like a wild fantasy, but the fact is that digital robots, controlled by algorithmic memes, have already colonized Mars—several decades before the first human body may get there.[71]

The digitalization of life is driven by strong commercial interests. Yet, it is we, the ordinary consumers, who drive the development. We are building the *Internet of Things* for our own convenience. Everything from clothing and light bulbs to cars, TVs, and satellites is connected to a worldwide digital network, and the most important *thing* is you and me.

Overall, the evolution of new technology seems unstoppable.[72] The development of AI and biotechnology is driven by our desire to live long and happy lives. And it is not just a humble wish. We literally demand that society should go to extreme lengths so that we and our loved ones can live as long as possible. The fight against cancer is a leading driver of both bio- and information technology. The fear of cancer and death is a powerful force, and few people question stem cell research or the development of artificial intelligence when the intention is to cure cancer. Why would anyone oppose the noble quest to rid the world of death and suffering?

It may seem like the obvious thing to do, but those who dream of a world without cancer may want to reconsider. The dream can come true, perhaps sooner than expected. The solution to cancer is possible, but it does not include human beings. At least not people of flesh and blood, who are born, grow up to have children of their own, and eventually die. To eliminate cancer "once and for all" means the end of all of this. Aging, cancer, and death are fundamental aspects of being human. If we eliminate this circle of life, we eliminate ourselves. We can design bodies that live forever and transfer our identity to the digital world, but we will no longer be human.

In the grand scheme of evolution, that may not be such a bad thing. Does it really matter if there are humans in a thousand years? Life has always evolved in new directions, and change is what evolution is all about. A growing social movement believes we should embrace this next step in human development. So-called *transhumanism* actively promotes technology that will bring our existence to a new level of development. On Wikipedia, we can read how transhumanists "believe that one should accelerate the course of evolution, radically improve human conditions with the help of scientific means and change society. Science must be utilized with great force to achieve this goal, especially neurotechnology, biotechnology and nanotechnology."[73] The ultimate goal is to free us from our mortal bodies and redefine what it means to be human.

Current technological developments strongly suggest that this is the direction we are heading. Humankind is just one step on the road to something more advanced. As we have already discussed, evolution is not really about us. The illusion that we are the center of the universe was shattered by Copernicus 400 years ago, and Darwin showed that we are just one of many stages in one of many branches in the tree of life.[74] The fact that genes and memes use biotechnology and artificial intelligence to develop more efficient life-forms is highly predictable. We are a means of transportation on a journey to where we do not know. In the ever-expanding universe, we are hardly more than an interesting curiosity—a ripple of low entropy in the periphery of one in about 100 billion galaxies.

In this evolutionary perspective, the solution to cancer is not the solution to *our* problems. We *are* the problem. Our slow, vulnerable, and perishable body stands in the way of the development of more efficient life-forms. The human body is yesterday's technology, and the bells are ringing for those of us who are still fond of good, old-fashioned people. We need to ask ourselves if today's technological development is really what we want. Do we have a choice, or are we doomed to make ourselves redundant?

In essence, the solution to cancer concerns our relationship with death. Death defines what it means to be human, but it is also our greatest limitation. We are facing a fundamental dilemma. Should we cure cancer and embrace transhumanism, or should we accept our own mortality and continue to be human? It is a difficult choice—if we have one. We are standing at a crossroad that will determine the future of our civilization.

Notes

CHAPTER 1

1. American Cancer Society, "Cancer Facts & Figures 2023," 2023, https://www.cancer.org/content/dam/cancer-org/research/cancer-facts-and-statistics/annual-cancer-facts-and-figures/2023/2023-cancer-facts-and-figures.pdf.

2. International Agency for Research on Cancer, "Cancer Today," 2023, https://gco.iarc.fr/today/home.

3. American Cancer Society, "Cancer Facts & Figures."

4. Theodosius Dobzhansky, "Nothing in Biology Makes Sense Except in the Light of Evolution," *American Biology Teacher* 35, no. 3 (March 1973): 125–29, https://doi.org/10.2307/4444260.

5. Thomas Kuhn, *The Structure of Scientific Revolutions* (50th ed.) (Chicago: University of Chicago Press, 2012).

6. Helen Dukas and Banesh Hoffmann, *Albert Einstein: The Human Side* (Princeton: Princeton University Press, 1979).

CHAPTER 2

1. Shazia Sarwar, "Norsk Løsning på kreftgåten" ["Norwegian Solution to the Cancer Mystery"], *VG*, October 5, 2015, https://www.vg.no/nyheter/meninger/i/82nRx/norsk-loesning-paa-kreftgaaten.

2. Sarwar, "Norwegian Solution to Cancer."

3. Gunnar Okstad, "De skal løse kreftgåten" ["They Are Going to Cure Cancer"], *Adresseavisen*, June 2019, https://www.adressa.no/okonomi/i/QymQWA/kjente-investorer-bak-norsk-kreftvaksineselskap.

4. State of the Union Address, 2016, The White House, USA, https://obamawhitehouse.archives.gov/the-press-office/2016/01/12/remarks-president-barack-obama-%E2%80%93-prepared-delivery-state-union-address.

5. J. Watkins, "Joe Biden and the Politics of Cancer" in *The Oxford Handbook of American Political Personalities*, edited by L. Huddy and D. Capelos (Oxford: Oxford University Press, 2021), 233–247.

6. F. Erik Brooks and MaCherie M. Placide, *Barack Obama: A Life in American History* (Santa Barbara: ABC-CLIO, 2019), http://publisher.abc-clio.com/9781440859144.

7. State of the Union Address, January 1970, The White House, USA, https://www.presidency.ucsb.edu/documents/annual-message-the-congress-the-state-the-union-2.

8. American Cancer Society, "Cancer Facts & Figures 2023," 2023, https://www.cancer.org/content/dam/cancer-org/research/cancer-facts-and-statistics/annual-cancer-facts-and-figures/2023/2023-cancer-facts-and-figures.pdf.

9. Jarle Breivik, "Who Has Misled Trond Mohn?" *Journal of the Norwegian Medical Association* 135 (January 2015): 558–60, https://tidsskriftet.no/en/2015/03/who-has-misled-trond-mohn.

10. Norwegian Institute of Public Health, "Cancer in Norway," 2014, https://www.fhi.no/nettpub/hin/ikke-smittsomme/kreft/?term=&h=1.

11. Breivik, "Who Has Misled Trond."

12. Jarle Breivik, "We Won't Cure Cancer," *New York Times*, May 27, 2016, https://www.nytimes.com/2016/05/27/opinion/obamas-pointless-cancer-moonshot.html.

13. Jarle Breivik, "Reframing the 'Cancer Moonshot': How Experts and Non-Experts Interpret the Problem of Cancer," *EMBO Reports* 17, no. 12 (December 2016): 1685–87, https://doi.org/10.15252/embr.201643467.

14. Bjarte Reve, "The Lance Armstrong Story in Oslo," *Forskning.no*, August 2009, https://blogg.forskning.no/bjarte-reve/the-lance-armstrong-story-i -oslo/1119519.

15. Lance Armstrong (@lancearmstrong), "Brutally honest oped from Prof Jarle Breivik," Twitter, May 27, 2016, 8:30 a.m., https://twitter.com/ lancearmstrong/status/736187773640531970.

16. Cancer Research UK, "Half a Million Lives Saved in 30 Years Thanks to Cancer Research," July 2013, https://news.cancerresearchuk. org/2013/07/09/half-a-million-lives-saved-in-30-years-thanks-to-cancer -research/.

17. Arthur Miller, *An Enemy of the People: An Adaptation of the Play by Henrik Ibsen* (New York: Penguin Books, 2010).

CHAPTER 3

1. Siddhartha Mukherjee, *The Emperor of All Maladies* (New York: Scribner, 2010).

2. Robert A. Aronowitz, *Unnatural History: Breast Cancer and American Society* (Cambridge: Cambridge University Press, 2007).

3. Matthew D. Freeman, Jared M. Gopman, and Andrew C. Salzberg, "The Evolution of Mastectomy Surgical Technique: From Mutilation to Medicine," *Gland Surgery* 7, no. 3 (June 2018): 308–15, doi: 10.21037/ gs.2017.09.07.

4. American Cancer Society, "Cancer Facts & Figures 2023," 2023, https:// www.cancer.org/content/dam/cancer-org/research/cancer-facts-and -statistics/annual-cancer-facts-and-figures/2023/2023-cancer-facts-and -figures.pdf.

5. Susan Sontag, *Illness as Metaphor* (New York: Farrar, Straus & Giroux, 1978).

6. Norwegian Cancer Society, "Fuck Cancer Bracelets," 2023, https:// nettbutikk.kreftforeningen.no/butikk/armband/armband-fuck-cancer/.

7. Guillem Rico, Marc Guinjoan, and Eva Anduiza, "The Emotional Underpinnings of Populism: How Anger and Fear Affect Populist Attitudes," *Swiss Political Science Review* 23, no. 4 (December 201): 111 61, https://onlinelibrary.wiley.com/doi/abs/10.1111/spsr.12261.

8. David Gardner, "Barack Obama's Beloved Grandmother Dies of Cancer on the Eve of the Presidential Election," *Mail Online*, November 4, 2008, https://www.dailymail.co.uk/news/article-1082775/Barack-Obamas -beloved-grandmother-dies-cancer-eve-presidential-election.html.

9. Norwegian Cancer Society, "Kampen er over" ["The Fight Is Over"], 2019, https://kreftforeningen.no/vitensenteret/kampen-er-over/.

10. Livestrong Foundation, accessed January 2022, https://www.livestrong.org/.

11. War on Cancer, accessed January 2022, https://waroncancer .com/.

12. Matthew Staff, "Swede's War on Cancer Moves to a Digital Battlefield," ComputerWeekly.com, January 2020, https://www.computerweekly.com/ news/252476337/Swedes-war-on-cancer-moves-to-a-digital-battlefield.

13. "Interview with Amalie Skram," *Verdens Gang* (1899), https://www.ordtak .no/sitat.php?id=9967.

CHAPTER 4.

1. Wikipedia, "Cancer" entry, last modified February 3, 2023, https:// en.wikipedia.org/wiki/Cancer.

2. *Encyclopedia Britannica*, "Cancer" entry, last modified February 3, 2023, https://www.britannica.com/science/cancer-disease.

3. Norwegian Cause of Death Registry, 2021, https://www.fhi .no/hn/helseregistre-og-registre/dodsarsaksregisteret/tall-fra -dodsarsaksregisteret-2021/.

4. Norwegian Ministry of Health and Care Services, "Principles for Priority Setting in Health Care," 2017, https://www.regjeringen. no/contentassets/439a420e01914a18b21f351143ccc6af/en-gb/pdfs/ stm201520160034000engpdfs.pdf.

5. Morten Magelssen, Reidun Førde, and Anders Tvedt, "Hvor mange kroner

er et godt leveår verdt?" ["How Many Kroner Is a Good Year of Life Worth?"], *Morgenbladet*, December 2018, https://www.morgenbladet.no/ideer/kronikk/2018/12/21/hvor-mange-kroner-er-ett-godt-levear-verdt/.

6. Allied Market Research, "Oncology/Cancer Drugs Market (2021)," https://www.alliedmarketresearch.com/oncology-cancer-drugs-market.

7. Richard Smith, "Dying of Cancer Is the Best Death," *The BMJ Opinion* (blog), December 31, 2014, https://blogs.bmj.com/bmj/2014/12/31/richard-smith-dying-of-cancer-is-the-best-death/.

8. Smith, "Dying of Cancer."

9. Smith, "Dying of Cancer."

10. Per Fugelli, *Døden, skal vi danse?* [*Death, Shall We Dance?*] (Oslo: Universitetsforlaget, 2010).

11. Fugelli, *Death, Shall We Dance?*

12. Fugelli, *Death, Shall We Dance?*

13. Nina Berglund, "Princess Refuses to Give Up Her Title," *NEWSinENGLISH.no*, May 16, 2019, https://www.newsinenglish.no/2019/05/16/princess-refuses-to-give-up-her-title/.

14. Emma Bubola and Henrik Pryser Libell, "Norwegian Princess Engaged to a Shaman Gives Up Her Royal Duties," *New York Times*, November 10, 2022, https://www.nytimes.com/2022/11/10/world/europe/norwegian-princess-martha-louise-durek-verrett.html.

15. Agence France, "Norwegian Princess Quits Royal Duties to Work with 'Shaman' Fiance," *The Guardian*, November 10, 2022, https://www.theguardian.com/world/2022/nov/08/norwegian-princess-quits-royal-duties-work-shaman-fiance-martha-louise.

16. Wikipedia, "Placebo" entry, last modified February 19, 2022, https://en.wikipedia.org/wiki/Placebo.

17. Anton J.M. de Craen, Pieter J. Roos, A. Leonard de Vries, & Jos Kleijnen, "Effect of Color of Drugs: Systematic Review of Perceived Effect of Drugs and of Their Effectiveness," *BMJ* 313 (1996): 1624–26, https://doi.org/10.1136/bmj.313.7072.1624.

18. David Colquhoun and Steven P. Novella, "Acupuncture Is Theatrical Placebo," *Anesthesia & Analgesia* 116, no. 6 (June 2013): 1360–63, https://doi.org/10.1213/ANE.0b013e31828f2d5e.

19. Sander van der Linden, "Misinformation: Susceptibility, Spread, and Interventions to Immunize the Public," *Nature Medicine* 28 (2022): 460–67, https://doi.org/10.1038/s41591-022-01713-, Michael A. Gisondi, Rachel Barber, Jemery Samuel Faust, Ali Raja, Matthew C. Strehlow, Lauren M. Westafer, and Michael Gottlieb, "A Deadly Infodemic: Social Media and the Power of COVID-19 Misinformation," Journal of Medical Internet Research 24, no. 2 (February 2022), https://doi.org/10.2196/35552.

20. Craig Murray, Nina von Possel, Hanne C. Lie, and Jarle Breivik, "The Nine Cancer Frames: A Tool to Facilitate Critical Reading of Cancer -Related Information," *Journal of Cancer Education* 37 (2022): 1918–27, https://doi.org/10.1007/s13187-021-02062-7.

21. May-Britt Moser and Edvard Moser, "WHERE AM I? WHERE AM I GOING?" *Scientific American* 314, no. 1 (January 2016): 26–33, doi: 10.1038/scientificamerican0116-26. PMID: 26887193.

22. György Buzsáki, "How the Brain 'Constructs' the Outside World?" *Scientific American* (June 2022), https://www.scientificamerican.com/article/how-the-brain-constructs-the-outside-world/.

23. David Linden, *Unique: The New Science of Human Individuality* (New York: Basic Books, 2020).

24. Wikipedia, "I Know That I Know Nothing," accessed February 19, 2023, https://en.wikipedia.org/wiki/I_know_that_I_know_nothing.

CHAPTER 5

1. American Cancer Society, "Health Risks of Smoking Tobacco," February 2023, https://www.cancer.org/healthy/stay-away-from-tobacco/health-risks-of-tobacco/health-risks-of-smoking-tobacco.html.

2. Yussuf Saloojee and Elif Dagli, "Tobacco Industry Tactics for Resisting Public Policy on Health," *Bulletin of the World Health Organization* 78, no. 7 (2000): 902–10, https://apps.who.int/iris/handle/10665/268182.

3. OECD, "Smoking among Adults," February 2023, https://www.oecd-ilibrary.org/sites/611b5b35-en/index.html?itemId=/content/component/611b5b35-en.

4. Helsedirektoratet, "Tobacco Control in Norway," February 2023, https://www.helsedirektoratet.no/english/tobacco-control-in-norway.

5. World Health Organization, "Tobacco: Industry Tactics to Attract Younger Generations," March 2020, https://www.who.int/news-room/questions-and-answers/item/tobacco-industry-tactics-to-attract-younger-generations.

6. Angel Fernandez-Flores and Eduardo Fonseca, "Scrotal Cancer, Chimney Sweepers and Sir Percival Pott," *Clinics in Dermatology* 40, no. 2 (2022): 209–20, https://doi.org/10.1016/j.clindermatol.2021.12.002.

7. Fernandez-Flores and Fonseca, "Scrotal Cancer, Chimney Sweepers."

8. National Cancer Institute, "Chemicals in Meat Cooked at High Temperatures and Cancer Risk," 2017, https://www.cancer.gov/about-cancer/causes-prevention/risk/diet/cooked-meats-fact-sheet.

9. Tom Reynolds, "Acrylamide and Cancer: Tunnel Leak in Sweden Prompted Studies," *Journal of the National Cancer Institute* 94, no. 12 (June 2002): 876–78, https://doi.org/10.1093/jnci/94.12.876.

10. European Food Safety Authority, "Acrylamide," May 2022, https://www.efsa.europa.eu/en/topics/topic/acrylamide.

11. Portia Bradford, "Skin Cancer in Skin of Color," *Dermatology Nursing* 21, no. 4 (2009): 170–78, https://www.ncbi.nlm.nih.gov/pmc/articles/PMC2757062/.

12. Wikipedia, "Gene–Environment Interaction" entry, accessed February 2023, https://en.wikipedia.org/wiki/Gene%E2%80%93environment_interaction.

13. Wikipedia, "BRCA Mutation" entry, accessed February 2023, https://en.wikipedia.org/wiki/BRCA_mutation.

14. Nina G. Jablonski and George Chaplin, "The Roles of Vitamin D and Cutaneous Vitamin D Production in Human Evolution and Health," *International Journal of Paleopathology* 23 (December 2018): 54–59, https://doi.org/10.1016/j.ijpp.2018.01.005.

15. Jing Liang and Yongfeng Shang, "Estrogen and Cancer," *Annual Review of Physiology* 75 (February 2013): 225–40, https://www.annualreviews.org/doi/abs/10.1146/annurev-physiol-030212-183708.

16. Wikipedia, "Human Papillomavirus Infection" entry, accessed February 2023, https://en.wikipedia.org/wiki/Human_papillomavirus_infection.

17. Wikipedia, "HPV vaccine" entry, accessed February 2023, https://en.wikipedia.org/wiki/HPV_vaccine.

18. Wikipedia, "Hodgkin Lymphoma" entry, accessed February 2023, https://en.wikipedia.org/wiki/Hodgkin_lymphoma.

19. Wikipedia, "Kaposi's Sarcoma" entry, accessed February 2023, https://en.wikipedia.org/wiki/Kaposi%27s_sarcoma.

20. Andrew Storfer, Paul A. Hohenlohe, Mark J. Margres, Austin Patton, Alexandra K. Fraik, Matthew Lawrance, Lauren E. Ricci, Amanda R. Stahlke, Hamish I. McCallum, and Menna E. Jones, "The Devil Is in the Details: Genomics of Transmissible Cancers in Tasmanian Devils," *PLoS Pathogens* 14, no. 8 (August 2018): e1007098, https://dx.doi.org/10.1371%2Fjournal.ppat.1007098.

21. Hannah Warren and Jonathon Olsburgh, "Management of Renal Cell Carcinoma and Other Renal Masses in the Kidney Graft," *Current Urology Reports* 21, no. 8 (2020), https://doi.org/10.1007/s11934-020-0959-4.

22. American Cancer Society, "Second Cancers Related to Treatment," February 2023, https://www.cancer.org/treatment/survivorship-during-and-after-treatment/long-term-health-concerns/second-cancers-in-adults/treatment-risks.html.

23. National Cancer Institute, "Late Effects of Cancer Treatment," February 2023, https://www.cancer.gov/about-cancer/coping/survivorship/late-effects.

24. Centers for Disease Control and Prevention, "Obesity and Cancer," February 2023, https://www.cdc.gov/cancer/obesity/index.htm.

25. National Cancer Institute, "Electromagnetic Fields and Cancer," February 2023, https://www.cancer.gov/about-cancer/causes-prevention/risk/radiation/electromagnetic-fields-fact-sheet.

26. National Cancer Institute, "Age and Cancer Risk," February 2023, https://www.cancer.gov/about-cancer/causes-prevention/risk/age.

27. Richard M. Martin, "Prostate Cancer Is Omnipresent, But Should We Screen for It?" *International Journal of Epidemiology* 36, no. 2 (April 2007): 278–81, https://academic.oup.com/ije/article/36/2/278/724857?login=true.

28. Max Roser, Esteban Ortiz-Ospina, and Hannah Ritchie, "Life

Expectancy," OurWorldInData.org, 2013, https://ourworldindata.org/
life-expectancy.

29. Renee Stepler, "World's Centenarian Population Projected to Grow
Eightfold by 2050," Pew Research Center, April 2016, http://pewrsr
.ch/22PVly7.

30. Kari Hemminki and Bowang Chen, "Familial Risks in Testicular Cancer
as Aetiological Clues," *International Journal of Andrology* 29, no. 1 (2006):
205–10, https://doi.org/10.1111/j.1365-2605.2005.00599.x.

31. Sam Harper, Corinne A. Riddell, and Nicholas B. King, "Declining Life
Expectancy in the United States: Missing the Trees for the Forest,"
Annual Review of Public Health 42, no. 1 (2021): 381–403, https://www
.annualreviews.org/doi/10.1146/annurev-publhealth-082619-104231.

32. William Shakespeare, edited by Sylvan Barnet, *Hamlet* (New York: Signet
Classics, 1998).

33. Ida Kvittingen, "Why Are Fewer Men Becoming Fathers than Before?"
ScienceNorway.no, November 9, 2020, https://sciencenorway.no/children
-and-adolescents-demography-gender-and-society/why-are-fewer-men
-becoming-fathers-than-before/1767348.

34. Wikipedia, "Incel" entry, accessed February 2023, https://en.wikipedia.org/
wiki/Incel.

35. Ciara Nugent, "What It Was Like to Grow Up as the World's First 'Test
-Tube Baby,'" *Time*, July 25, 2018, https://time.com/5344145/louise-brown
-test-tube-baby/.

36. Hans Ivar Hanevik, Dag O. Hessen, Arne Sunde, and Jarle Breivik, "Can
IVF Influence Human Evolution?" *Human Reproduction* 31, no. 7 (July
2016): 1397–1402, https://doi.org/10.1093/humrep/dew089.

37. Wikipedia, "Designer Baby" entry, accessed February 2023, https://
en.wikipedia.org/wiki/Designer_baby.

38. Wikipedia, "Abortion Law" entry, accessed February 2023, https://
en.wikipedia.org/wiki/Abortion_law.

39. S. Matthew Liao, "The Embryo Rescue Case," *Theoretical Medicine
and Bioethics* 27 (April 2006): 141–47, https://link.springer.com/
article/10.1007%2Fs11017-005-1390-z.

40. Thomas W. Sadler, *Langman's Medical Embryology, 14th ed.* (Philadelphia: Wolters Kluwer Health, 2018).

41. Sadler, *Langman's Medical Embryology.*

42. Sadler, *Langman's Medical Embryology.*

43. Elizabeth Landau, "How Much Did Grandmothers Influence Human Evolution?" *Smithsonian Magazine,* January 4, 2021, https://www. smithsonianmag.com/science-nature/how-much-did-grandmothers -influence-human-evolution-180976665/.

44. Wikipedia, "Disposable Soma Theory of Aging" entry, accessed January 2022, https://en.wikipedia.org/wiki/Disposable_soma_theory_of_aging.

CHAPTER 6

1. Charles Darwin, *On the Origin of Species* (London: John Murray, 1859).

2. Wikipedia, "Jean-Baptiste Lamarck" entry, accessed February 2023, https://en.wikipedia.org/wiki/Jean-Baptiste_Lamarck.

3. Wikipedia, "Eugenics" entry, accessed February 2023, https://en.wikipedia .org/wiki/Eugenics.

4. Elof Axel Carlson, *The Unfit: A History of a Bad Idea* (Cold Spring Harbor, NY: Cold Spring Harbor Laboratory Press, 2021).

5. Siri Haavie, "Sterilization in Norway—A Dark Chapter?" Samtiden, 2003, https://www.eurozine.com/sterilization-in-norway-a-dark-chapter/?pdf.

6. The Associated Press, "China Cuts Uighur Births with Iuds, Abortion, Sterilization," June 28, 2020, https://apnews.com/article/ap-top-news -international-news-weekend-reads-china-health-269b3de1af34e17c1941a 514f78d764c.

7. Wikipedia, "War Crimes of the Wehrmacht" entry, accessed February 2023, https://en.wikipedia.org/wiki/War_crimes_of_the_Wehrmacht.

8. Richard Weikart, *From Darwin to Hitler: Evolutionary Ethics, Eugenics, and Racism in Germany* (London: Palgrave Macmillan, 2004).

9. Eörs Szathmáry, "The Origin of Replicators and Reproducers," *Royal Society* 361, no. 1474 (October 2006): 1761–76, https://doi .org/10.1098%2Frstb.2006.1912.

10. Leslie A. Pray, "Discovery of DNA Structure and Function: Watson and

Crick," *Nature Education* 1, no. 1 (2008), https://www.nature.com/scitable/topicpage/discovery-of-dna-structure-and-function-watson-397/.

11. James D. Watson and Francis H.C. Crick, "A Structure for Deoxyribose Nucleic Acid," *Nature* 171, (1953): 737–38, https://www.nature.com/scitable/content/Molecular-Structure-of-Nucleic-Acids-16331.

12. Jarle Breivik, "Self-Organization of Template-Replicating Polymers and the Spontaneous Rise of Genetic Information," *Entropy* 3, no. 4 (2001): 273–79, https://doi.org/10.3390/e3040273.

13. Breivik, "Self-Organization of Template."

14. Wikipedia, "Gene" entry, accessed February 2023, https://en.wikipedia.org/wiki/Gene.

15. Michael Marshall, "How the First Life on Earth Survived Its Biggest Threat—Water," *Nature* 588 (2020): 210–13, https://www.nature.com/articles/d41586-020-03461-4.

16. Wikipedia, "Gene-centered View of Evolution" entry, accessed February 2023, https://en.wikipedia.org/wiki/Gene-centered_view_of_evolution.

17. Richard Dawkins, *The Selfish Gene* (Oxford: Oxford University Press, 1976).

18. Itai Yanai and Martin J. Lercher, "Forty Years of *The Selfish Gene* Are Not Enough," *Genome Biology* 17, no. 39 (March 2016), https://doi.org/10.1186/s13059-016-0910-7.

19. Wikipedia, "Polymerase Chain Reaction" entry, accessed February 2023, https://en.wikipedia.org/wiki/Polymerase_chain_reaction.

20. Jarle Breivik, Gunn Iren Meling, Anne Spurkland, Torleiv O. Rognum, and Gustav Gaudernack, "K-ras Mutation in Colorectal Cancer: Relations to Patient Age, Sex and Tumour Location," *British Journal of Cancer* 69 (1994): 367–71, https://www.nature.com/articles/bjc199467#citeas.

21. Dawkins, *The Selfish Gene*.

22. Jeremy Lent, "It's Time to Consign the 'Selfish Gene' to the History Books," *Salon*, May 30, 2021, https://www.salon.com/2021/05/30/its-time-to-consign-the-selfish-gene-to-the-history-books/.

23. Matt Ridley, "In Retrospect: *The Selfish Gene*," *Nature* 529 (January 2016): 462–63, https://www.nature.com/articles/529462a.

24. Alan Grafen and Mark Ridley, *Richard Dawkins: How a Scientist Changed the Way We Think* (Oxford: Oxford University Press, 2007).

25. Richard Dawkins, *God Delusion* (New York: Bantam Books, 2006).

26. Wikipedia, "Thomas Henry Huxley" entry, accessed February 2023, https://en.wikipedia.org/wiki/Thomas_Henry_Huxley.

27. Theodosius Dobzhansky, "Nothing in Biology Makes Sense Except in the Light of Evolution," American Biology Teacher 35, no. 3 (March 1973): 125–29, https://doi.org/10.2307/4444260.

28. Pardis Sabeti, "Natural Selection: Uncovering Mechanisms of Evolutionary Adaptation to Infectious Disease," *Nature Education* 1, no. 1 (2008): 13, https://www.nature.com/scitable/topicpage/natural-selection-uncovering -mechanisms-of-evolutionary-adaptation-34539/.

29. Sabeti, "Natural Selection: Uncovering Mechanisms."

CHAPTER 7

1. Thomas W. Sadler, Langman's Medical Embryology, 14th ed. (Philadelphia: Wolters Kluwer Health, 2018)..

2. Ross C. Hardison, "Evolution of Hemoglobin and Its Genes," *Cold Spring Harbor Perspectives in Medicine* 2, no. 12 (2012): a011627, https://www.ncbi .nlm.nih.gov/pmc/articles/PMC3543078/.

3. Daniel E. Koshland Jr., "Molecule of the Year 1993," *Science* 262, no. 5142 (1994): 1953, https://www.science.org/doi/10.1126/science.8266084.

4. Arnold J. Levine, "800 Million Years of Evolution and 40 Years of Discovery," *Nature Reviews Cancer* 20 (May 2020): 471–80, https://doi .org/10.1038/s41568-020-0262-1.

5. DP Lane, "p53, Guardian of the Genome," *Nature* 358 (1992): 15–16, https://www.nature.com/articles/358015a0.

6. Allal Ouhtit, Hisayoshi Nakazawa, Hiroshi Yamasaki, Bruce K. Armstrong, Anne Kricker, Ernest Tan, and Dallas R. English, "UV-Radiation-Specific p53 Mutation Frequency in Normal Skin as a Predictor of Risk of Basal Cell Carcinoma," *Journal of the National Cancer Institute* 90, no. 7 (April 1998): 523–31, https://doi.org/10.1093/jnci/90.7.523.

7. National Cancer Institute, "What Is Cancer?" accessed February 2023, https://www.cancer.gov/about-cancer/understanding/what-is-cancer.

8. Jarle Breivik, "The Evolutionary Origin of Genetic Instability in Cancer

Development," *Seminars in Cancer Biology* 15, no. 1 (2005): 51–60, https://doi.org/10.1016/j.semcancer.2004.09.008.

9. Niels Kaj Jerne, "The Natural-Selection Theory of Antibody Formation," *Proceedings of the National Academy USA* 41, no. 11 (1955): 849–57, https://doi.org/10.1073/pnas.41.11.849.

10. Alla Katsnelson, "What Do We Know about the Novel Coronavirus's 29 Proteins?" *c & en* (2020), https://cen.acs.org/biological-chemistry/infectious-disease/know-novel-coronaviruss-29-proteins/98/web/2020/04.

11. Jerne, "The Natural-Selection Theory."

12. David G. Schatz and Yanhong Ji, "Recombination Centers and the Orchestration of V(D)J Recombination," *Nature Reviews Immunology* 11, no. 2 (2011): 251–63, https://www.nature.com/articles/nri2941.

13. Jill E. Kucab, Xueqing Zou, Sandro Morganella, Madeleine Joel, A. Scott Nanda, Eszter Nagy, Celine Gomez, et al., "A Compendium of Mutational Signatures of Environmental Agents," *Cell* 177, no. 4 (May 2019): 821–36, https://www.ncbi.nlm.nih.gov/pmc/articles/PMC6506336/.

14. Nathaniel Scharping, "How Are Neanderthals Different from Homo Sapiens?" *Discover*, May 2020, https://www.discovermagazine.com/planet-earth/how-are-neanderthals-different-from-homo-sapiens.

15. Scharping, "How Are Neanderthals Different."

16. Breivik, "Evolutionary Origin of Genetic Instability."

17. Satoshi Oota, "Somatic Mutations—Evolution within the Individual," *Methods* 176 (April 2020): 91–98, https://doi.org/10.1016/j.ymeth.2019.11.002.

18. Cristian Tomasetti, Lu Li, and Bert Vogelstein, "Stem Cell Divisions, Somatic Mutations, Cancer Etiology, and Cancer Prevention," *Science* 355, no. 6331 (March 2017): 1330–34, https://doi.org/10.1126/science.aaf9011.

19. Tomasetti, "Stem Cell Divisions."

20. Jennifer Couzin-Frankel, "Debate Reignites over the Contributions of 'Bad Luck' Mutations to Cancer," *Science*, March 23, 2017, https://www.science.org/content/article/debate-reignites-over-contributions-bad-luck-mutations-cancer.

21. Martin A. Nowak and Bartlomiej Waclaw, "Genes, Environment, and 'Bad Luck,'" *Science* 355, no. 6331 (March 2017): 1266–67, https://doi.org/10.1126/science.aam9746.

22. W.D. Riggs, "Luck, Knowledge, and 'Mere' Coincidence," *Metaphilosophy* 45, no. 4–5 (October 2014): 627–39, https://doi.org/10.1111/meta.12109.

23. Cristian Tomasetti and Bert Vogelstein, "Variation in Cancer Risk among Tissues Can Be Explained by the Number of Stem Cell Divisions," Science 347, no. 6217 (January 2015): 78–81, https://doi.org/10.1126/science.1260825.

24. Jerry W. Shay and Woodring E. Wright, "Telomeres and Telomerase: Three Decades of Progress," *Nature Reviews Genetics* 20 (February 2019): 299–309, https://www.nature.com/articles/s41576-019-0099-1.

25. Patricia A. Muller and Karen H. Vousden, "p53 Mutations in Cancer," *Nature Cell Biology* 15 (January 2013): 2–8, https://www.nature.com/articles/ncb2641.

26. Breivik, "Evolutionary Origin of Genetic Instability."

27. Jarle Breivik, Gunn Iren Meling, Anne Spurkland, Torleiv O. Rognum, and Gustav Gaudernack, "K-ras Mutation in Colorectal Cancer: Relations to Patient Age, Sex and Tumour Location," British Journal of Cancer 69 (1994): 367–71, https://www.nature.com/articles/bjc199467#citeas.

28. Jarle Breivik, Ragnhild A. Lothe, Gunn Iren Meling, Torleiv O. Rognum, Anne-Lise Børresen-Dale, and Gustav Gaudernack, "Different Genetic Pathways to Proximal and Distal Colorectal Cancer Influenced by Sex-Related Factors," *International Journal of Cancer* 74, no. 6 (December 1998): 664–69, https://doi.org/10.1002/(sici)1097-0215(19971219)74:6%3C664::aid-ijc18%3E3.0.co;2-5.

29. Jarle Breivik and Gustav Gaudernack, "Carcinogenesis and Natural Selection: A New Perspective to the Genetics and Epigenetics of Colorectal Cancer," *Advances in Cancer Research* 76 (1999): 187–212, https://doi.org/10.1016/s0065-230x(08)60777-0.

30. Couzin-Frankel, "Debate Reignites."

31. Alberto Bardelli, Daniel P. Cahill, Gabi Lederer, Michael R. Speicher, Kenneth W. Kinzler, Bert Vogelstein, and Christoph Lengauer, "Carcinogen-Specific Induction of Genetic Instability," *Proceedings of the National Academy of Sciences USA* 98, no. 10 (2001): 5770–75, https://doi.org/10.1073/pnas.081082898.

32. Bardelli, "Carcinogen-Specific Induction."

33. Jarle Breivik and Gustav Gaudernack, "Don't Stop for Repairs in a War

Zone: Darwinian Evolution Unites Genes and Environment in Cancer Development," *Proceedings of the National Academy of Sciences USA* 98, no. 10 (May 2001): 5379–81, https://doi.org/10.1073/pnas.101137698.

34. Jarle Breivik, "Cancer—Evolution Within," *International Journal of Epidemiology* 35, no. 5 (2006): 1161–62, https://doi.org/10.1093/ije/dyl187.

35. Carl Zimmer, "Evolved for Cancer?" *Scientific American,* July 2008, https://www.scientificamerican.com/article/evolved-for-cancer-2008-07/.

CHAPTER 8

1. Thomas W. Sadler, *Langman's Medical Embryology, 14th ed.* (Philadelphia: Wolters Kluwer Health, 2018).

2. Wikipedia, "DNA Methylation" entry, accessed February 23, 2023, https://en.wikipedia.org/wiki/DNA_methylation.

3. Nataliya Petryk, Sebastian Bultmann, Till Bartke, and Pierre-Antoine Defossez, "Staying True to Yourself: Mechanisms of DNA Methylation Maintenance in Mammals," *Nucleic Acids Research* 49, no. 6 (April 2021): 3020–32, https://doi.org/10.1093/nar/gkaa1154.

4. Apolline Imbard, Jean-Francois Benoist, and Henk J. Blom, "Neural Tube Defects, Folic Acid and Methylation," *International Journal of Environmental Research and Public Health* 10, no. 9 (September 2013): 4352–89, https://doi.org/10.3390%2Fijerph10094352.

5. Shahjehan A. Wajed, Peter W. Laird, and Tom R. DeMeester, "DNA Methylation: An Alternative Pathway to Cancer," *Annals of Surgery* 234, no. 1 (July 2001): 10–20, https://doi.org/10.1097/00000658-200107000-0000; Wikipedia, "DNA Methylation in Cancer" entry, accessed February 23, 2023, https://en.wikipedia.org/wiki/DNA_methylation_in_cancer.

6. Jenny Graves, Neil Murray, and Nick Murphy, "No, Epigenetics and Environmental Responsiveness Do Not Undermine Darwinian Evolution," *The Conversation*, April 25, 2017, https://theconversation.com/no-epigenetics-and-environmental-responsiveness-dont-undermine-darwinian-evolution-65647.

7. Wikipedia, "Histone Code" entry, accessed January 2022, https://en.wikipedia.org/wiki/Histone_code.

8. Wikipedia, "Internet Meme" entry, accessed January 2022, https:// en.wikipedia.org/wiki/Internet_meme.

9. Richard Dawkins, *The Selfish Gene* (Oxford: Oxford University Press, 1976).

10. Charles Q. Choi, "Ape See, Ape Do: Chimps Learn Skills from Each Other," *Live Science*, September 30, 2014, https://www.livescience .com/48078-chimpanzees-learn-behaviors-socially.html.

11. Susan Blackmore, *The Meme Machine* (Oxford: Oxford University Press, 2000).

12. Wikipedia, "Critics of Memetics" entry, accessed February 2023, https:// en.wikipedia.org/wiki/Memetics#Critics_of_memetics.

13. Heimskringla Hávamál, https://heimskringla.no/wiki/ H%C3%A5vam%C3%A5l.

14. Michel Sabe, Chaomei Chen, Othman Sentissi, Jeroen Deenik, Davy Vancampfort, Joseph Firth, Lee Smith, et al., "Thirty Years of Research on Physical Activity, Mental Health, and Wellbeing: A Scientometric Analysis of Hotspots and Trends," *Frontiers in Public Health* 10 (August 2022), https:// doi.org/10.3389/fpubh.2022.943435.

15. Walker Percy, "The Existential Dane," *New York Times*, April 1, 1979, https://www.nytimes.com/1979/04/01/archives/the-existential-dane-the -dane.html.

16. Caitlin Aamodt, Madza Farias-Virgens, and Stephanie A. White, "Birdsong as a Window into Language Origins and Evolutionary Neuroscience," *Philosophical Transactions of the Royal Society B.* 375, no. 1789 (January 2020), https://doi.org/10.1098/rstb.2019.0060.

17. Christoph Adami, "What Is Information?" *Philosophical Transactions of the Royal Society A.* 374, no. 2063 (March 2016), https://doi.org/10.1098/ rsta.2015.0230.

18. Stephen Hawking, *The Universe in a Nutshell* (New York: Bantam, 2001).

19. Adami, "What Is Information?"

20. Rolf Landauer, "Information Is Physical," *Physics Today* 44, no. 5 (1991): 23, https://doi.org/10.1063/1.881299.

21. Yongsheng Liu and Qi Chen, "150 Years of Darwin's Theory of Intercellular Flow of Hereditary Information," *Nature Reviews Molecular*

Cell Biology 19, no. 12 (November 2018): 749–50, https://doi.org/10.1038/s41580-018-0072-4.

22. Nina Berglund, "Princess Refuses to Give Up Her Title," *NEWSinENGLISH.no*, May 16, 2019, https://www.newsinenglish.no/2019/05/16/princess-refuses-to-give-up-her-title/.

23. Reema Abdulrahman S. Alyamani and Christ Murgatroyd, "Epigenetic Programming by Early-Life Stress," *Progress in Molecular Biology and Translational Science* 157 (2018): 133–50, https://doi.org/10.1016/bs.pmbts.2018.01.004.

24. Farzeen Kader, Meenu Ghai, and Leah Maharaj, "The Effects of DNA Methylation on Human Psychology," *Behavioural Brain Research* 346 (July 2018): 47–65, https://doi.org/10.1016/j.bbr.2017.12.004.

25. Suzanne C. Segerstrom and Gregory E. Miller, "Psychological Stress and the Human Immune System: A Meta-Analytical Study of 30 Years of Inquiry," *Psychological Bulletin* 130, no. 4 (2004): 601–30, https://dx.doi.org/10.1037%2F0033-2909.130.4.601.

26. Timothy G. Dinan and John F. Cryan, "Microbes, Immunity, and Behavior: Psychoneuroimmunology Meets the Microbiome," *Neuropsychopharmacology* 42 (June 2016): 178–92, https://doi.org/10.1038/npp.2016.103.

27. Nora Wiium and Bente Wold, "Family and School Influences on Adolescent Smoking Behaviour," *Health Education* 106, no. 6 (2006): 465–79, https://doi.org/10.1108/09654280610711415.

28. Christian P. Schaaf, "Nicotinic Acetylcholine Receptors in Human Genetic Disease," *Genetics in Medicine* 16, no. 9 (2014): 649–56, https://doi.org/10.1038/gim.2014.9.

29. Tess McClure, "New Zealand Passes World-First Tobacco Law to Ban Smoking for Next Generation," *The Guardian*, December 13, 2023, https://www.theguardian.com/world/2022/dec/13/new-zealand-passes-world-first-tobacco-law-to-ban-smoking-by-2025.

30. Suzanne K. Chambers, Jeffrey Dunn, Stefano Occhipinti, Suzanne Hughes, Peter Baade, Sue Sinclair, Joanne Aitken, Pip Youl, and Dianne L. O'Connell, "A Systematic Review of the Impact of Stigma and Nihilism on Lung Cancer Outcomes," *BMC Cancer* 12, no. 184 (2012), https://doi.org/10.1186/1471-2407-12-184.

31. Doris Lessing, *The Four-Gated City* (London: MacGibbon & Kee, 1969).

32. Yan Cheng, Yingying Cai, Haomai Chen, Zhuang Cai, Gang Wu, and Jing Huang, "A Cognitive Level Evaluation Method Based on a Deep Neural Network for Online Learning: From a Bloom's Taxonomy of Cognition Objectives Perspective," *Frontiers in Psychology* 12 (2021), https://www .frontiersin.org/article/10.3389/fpsyg.2021.661235.

CHAPTER 9

1. "Askeavkok til besvær" ["Troubling Ash Decoction"], *Journal of the Norwegian Medical Association* 123, no. 750 (2003), https://tidsskriftet .no/2003/03/tidligere-i-tidsskriftet/askeavkok-til-besvaer.

2. Botanical.com, "Ash," February 24, 2023, https://www.botanical.com/ botanical/mgmh/a/ash--073.html.

3. Jessica Brown, "Are There Benefits to Eating Turmeric and Other Spices?" BBC.com, April 7, 2020, https://www.bbc.com/future/article/20200406 -are-there-benefits-to-eating-turmeric-and-other-spices.

4. Kathryn M. Nelson, Jayme L. Dahlin, Jonathan Bisson, James Graham, Guido F. Pauli, and Michael A. Walters, "The Essential Medicinal Chemistry of Curcumin," *Journal of Medicinal Chemistry* 60, no. 5 (January 2017): 1620–37, https://doi.org/10.1021/acs.jmedchem.6b00975.

5. Wikipedia, "Bharat Aggarwal" entry, accessed January 2022, https:// en.wikipedia.org/wiki/Bharat_Aggarwal#Scientific_misconduct.

6. Bonnie Annis, "Examining Turmeric's Role in Fighting Cancer," *Cure Today*, July 21, 2016, https://www.curetoday.com/view/could-turmeric-be-a -viable-alternative-for-fighting-cancer.

7. Kellie Bramlet Blackburn, "The Keto Diet and Cancer: What Patients Should Know," MD Anderson Cancer Center, April 2018, https://www .mdanderson.org/cancerwise/the-keto-diet-and-cancer--what-patients -should-know.h00-159223356.html.

8. Luigi L. Capasso, "Antiquity of Cancer," *International Journal of Cancer* 113, no. 1 (January 2005): 2–13, https://onlinelibrary.wiley.com/doi/ abs/10.1002/ijc.20610.

9. Karen Hardy, Jennie Brand-Miller, Katherine D. Brown, Mark G. Thomas, Les Copeland, and Daniel E. Dykhuizen, "The Importance of

Dietary Carbohydrate in Human Evolution," *The Quarterly Review of Biology* 90, no. 3 (September 2015): 251–68, https://www.journals.uchicago.edu/ doi/abs/10.1086/682587.

10. James A. Fellows Yates, Irina M. Velsko, Franziska Aron, and Christina Warinner, "The Evolution and Changing Ecology of the African Hominid Oral Microbiome," *Proceedings of the National Academy of Sciences USA* 118, no. 20 (May 2021), https://doi.org/10.1073/pnas.2021655118.

11. Sam Apple, *Ravenous: Otto Warburg, the Nazis, and the Search for the Cancer Diet Connection* (New York: Liveright Publishing Corporation, 2021).

12. Wikipedia, "Positron Emission Tomography" entry, accessed February 2023, https://en.wikipedia.org/wiki/Positron_emission_tomography.

13. Blackburn, "The Keto Diet."

14. National Cancer Institute, "Eating Hints: Before, during, and after Cancer Treatment," 2022, https://www.cancer.gov/publications/patient-education/ eating-hints.

15. U.S. Department of Agriculture, "Dietary Guidelines for Americans 2020–2025," 2022, https://www.dietaryguidelines.gov/resources/2020 -2025-dietary-guidelines-online-materials.

16. Orsolya Vincze, Fernando Colchero, Jean-Francois Lemaître, Dalia A. Conde, Samuel Pavard, Margaux Bieuville, Araxi O. Urrutia, et al., "Cancer Risk across Mammals," *Nature* 601 (December 2022): 263–67, https://doi.org/10.1038/s41586-021-04224-5.

17. Wikipedia, "Galápagos Tortoise" entry, accessed February 2023, https:// en.wikipedia.org/wiki/Gal%C3%A1pagos_tortoise.

18. Wikipedia, "Greenland Shark" entry, accessed February 2023, https:// en.wikipedia.org/wiki/Greenland_shark.

19. Roberto Ferrari, Gianluca Campo, Elisa Gardini, Giovanni Pasanisi, and Claudio Ceconi, "Specific and Selective If Inhibition: Expected Clinical Benefits from Pure Heart Rate Reduction in Coronary Patients," *European Heart Journal Supplements* 7, suppl_H (September 2005): H16–H21, https:// doi.org/10.1093/eurheartj/sui048.

20. Wikipedia, "Greenland Shark."

21. Paul M. L. Janssen, Brandon J. Biesiadecki, Mark T. Ziolo, and Jonathan P. Davis, "The Need for Speed: Mice, Men, and Myocardial Kinetic Reserve," *Circulation Research* 119, no. 3 (July 2016): 418–21, https://doi .org/10.1161/circresaha.116.309126.

22. Elizabeth Pennisi, "Why Naked Mole Rats Don't Get Cancer," *Science,* June 19, 2013, https://www.science.org/content/article/why-naked-mole-rats-dont-get-cancer.

23. Wikipedia, "Naked Mole-Rat" entry, accessed January 2022, https://en.wikipedia.org/wiki/Naked_mole-rat.

24. Andrii I. Rozhok and James DeGregori, "The Evolution of Lifespan and Age-Dependent Cancer Risk," *Trends in Cancer* 2, no. 10 (October 2016): 552–60, https://doi.org/10.1016/j.trecan.2016.09.004.

25. The Cryonics Institute, February 25, 2023, https://www.cryonics.org/.

26. Wikipedia, "Meristem" entry, accessed January 2022, https://en.wikipedia.org/wiki/Meristem.

27. Huimin Ma, Teng Song, Tianhua Wang, and Shui Wang, "Influence of Human p53 on Plant Development," *PLoS One* 11, no. 9 (September 2016): e0162840, https://doi.org/10.1371%2Fjournal.pone.0162840.

28. Barry E. Flanary and Gunther Kletetschka, "Analysis of Telomere Length and Telomerase Activity in Tree Species of Various Lifespans, and with Age in the Bristlecone Pine Pinus Longaeva," *Biogerontology* 6 (March 2005): 101–11, https://doi.org/10.1007/s10522-005-3484-4.

29. Wikipedia, "List of Oldest Trees" entry, accessed January 2022, https://en.wikipedia.org/wiki/List_of_oldest_trees.

30. Shazia Sarwar, "Norsk Løsning på kreftgåten" ["Norwegian Solution to the Cancer Mystery"], *VG,* October 5, 2015, https://www.vg.no/nyheter/meninger/i/82nRx/norsk-loesning-paa-kreftgaaten.

31. Philipp Dettmer, *Immune: A Journey into the Mysterious System That Keeps You Alive* (New York: Random House, 2021).

32. Puspa Thapa and Donna L. Farber, "The Role of the Thymus in the Immune Response," *Thoracic Surgery Clinics* 29, no. 2 (May 2019): 123–31, https://dx.doi.org/10.1016%2Fj.thorsurg.2018.12.001.

33. M.K. Gjertsen and Gustav Gaudernack, "Mutated Ras Peptides as Vaccines in Immunotherapy of Cancer," *Vox Sanguinis* 74, no. 2 (June 1998): 489–95, https://doi.org/10.1111/j.1423-0410.1998.tb05462.x.

34. Marianne K. Gjertsen, Arne Bakka, Jarle Breivik, Ingvil Saeterdal, Bjarte G. Solheim, Odd Søreide, Erik Thorsby, and Gustav Gaudernack,

"Vaccination with Mutant Ras Peptides and Induction of T-Cell Responsiveness in Pancreatic Carcinoma Patients Carrying the Corresponding RAS Mutation," *Lancet* 346 (November 1995): 1399–1400, https://doi.org/10.1016/s0140-6736(95)92408-6.

35. Espen Basmo Ellingsen, Sara M. Mangsbo, Eivind Hovig, and Gustav Gaudernack, "Telomerase as a Target for Therapeutic Cancer Vaccines and Considerations for Optimizing Their Clinical Potential," *Frontiers in Immunology* 12 (July 2021), https://doi.org/10.3389/fimmu.2021.682492.

36. "The Innovative Force behind Ultimovacs' Cancer Vaccine," *BioStock*, December 13, 2022, https://www.biostock.se/en/2022/12/den-innovativa-kraften-bakom-ultimovacs-cancervaccin/.

37. Pei-Wei Huang and John Wen-Cheng Chang, "Immune Checkpoint Inhibitors Win the 2018 Nobel Prize," *Biomedical Journal* 42, no. 5 (October 2019): 299–306, https://doi.org/10.1016/j.bj.2019.09.002.

38. Filipe Martins, Latifyan Sofiya, Gerasimos P. Sykiotis, Faiza Lamine, Michel Maillard, Montserrat Fraga, Keyvan Shabafrouz, et al., "Adverse Effects of Immune-Checkpoint Inhibitors: Epidemiology, Management and Surveillance," *Nature Reviews Clinical Oncology* 16 (May 2019): 563–80, https://doi.org/10.1038/s41571-019-0218-0.

39. Wikipedia, "Red Queen Hypothesis" entry, accessed January 2022, https://en.wikipedia.org/wiki/Red_Queen_hypothesis.

40. Atul Gawande, *Being Mortal* (London: Profile Books Ltd, 2015).

41. Wikipedia, "Hematopoietic Stem Cell Transplantation" entry, accessed January 2023, https://en.wikipedia.org/wiki/Hematopoietic_stem_cell_transplantation.

42. Chung-Mau Lo, "Transplantation for Liver Cancer—More with Better Results," *Nature Reviews Gastroenterology & Hepatology* 10, no. 2 (January 2013): 74–76, https://doi.org/10.1038/nrgastro.2012.257.

43. Mettu Srinivas Reddy, Joy Varghese, Jayanthi Venkataraman, and Mohamed Rela, "Matching Donor to Recipient in Liver Transplantation: Relevance in Clinical Practice," *World Journal of Hepatology* 5, no. 11 (November 2013): 603–11, http://dx.doi.org/10.4254/wjh.v5.i11.603.

44. Sara Reardon, "First Pig-to-Human Heart Transplant: What Can Scientists Learn?" *Nature* 601 (January 2022): 305–306, https://doi.org/10.1038/d41586-022-00111-9.

45. David K. C. Cooper, Takayuki Yamamoto, Hidetaka Hara, and Richard N. Pierson III, "The First Clinical Pig Heart Transplant: Was IVIg or Pig Cytomegalovirus Detrimental to the Outcome?" *Xenotransplantation* 29, no. 4 (July/August 2022): e12771, https://doi.org/10.1111/xen.12771.

46. Barbara Pfeffer Billauer, "Coming Soon: Head Transplants—Or Whose Body Is It?" American Council on Science and Health, June 21, 2022, https://www.acsh.org/news/2022/06/21/coming-soon-head-transplants -%E2%80%93-or-whose-body-it-16380.

47. Vahid Mansouri, Nima Beheshtizadeh, Maliheh Gharibshahian, Leila Sabouri, Mohammad Varzandeh, and Nima Rezaei, "Recent Advances in Regenerative Medicine Strategies for Cancer Treatment," *Biomedicine & Pharmacotherapy* 141 (September 2021): 111875, https://doi.org/10.1016/j .biopha.2021.111875.

48. Sayaka Wakayama, Hiroshi Ohta, Takafusa Hikichi, and Teruhiko Wakayama, "Production of Healthy Cloned Mice from Bodies Frozen at -20 Degrees C for 16 Years," *Proceedings of the National Academy of Sciences USA* 105, no. 45 (November 2008): 17318–22, https://doi.org/10.1073/ pnas.0806166105.

49. Wikipedia, "Savior Sibling" entry, accessed February 2023, https:// en.wikipedia.org/wiki/Savior_sibling.

50. Jarle Breivik, "Bioteknologiens katastrofale dilemma" ["The Catastrophic Dilemma of Biotechnology"], Dagens Næringsliv, July 22, 2022, https:// www.dn.no/innlegg/bioteknologi/kreftforeningen/kreftforskning/innlegg -bioteknologiens-katastrofale-dilemma/2-1-1261419.

51. Cadie Thompson, "6 Billionaires Who Want to Live Forever," *Insider,* September 2, 2015, https://www.businessinsider.com/billionaires-who-want -to-live-forever-2015-9?r=US&IR=T.

52. Daniel M. Davis, "Jeff Bezos Is Looking to Defy Death—This Is What We Know about the Science of Ageing," *The Conversation,* January 21, 2022, https://theconversation.com/jeff-bezos-is-looking-to-defy-death-this-is -what-we-know-about-the-science-of-ageing-175379.

53. E. Kumar Sharma, "Quest for Immortality," *Business Today*, October 20, 2019, https://www.businesstoday.in/magazine/luxury-special-2019/story/ quest-for-immortality-229591-2019-09-30.

54. Raj Chetty, Michael Stepner, Sarah Abraham, Shelby Lin, Benjamin

Scuderi, Nicholas Turner, Augustin Bergeron, and David Cutler, "The Association between Income and Life Expectancy in the United States, 2001–2014," *JAMA* 315, no. 16 (April 2016): 1750–66, https://doi.org/10.1001/jama.2016.4226.

55. Steve Jobs, "Death Is Very Likely the Single Best Invention of Life," *The Guardian*, October 6, 2011, https://www.theguardian.com/technology/2011/oct/06/steve-jobs-pancreas-cancer.

56. Wikipedia, "Memento Mori" entry, accessed January 2022, https://en.wikipedia.org/wiki/Memento_mori.

57. Alex Beam, "Will We Be the Last Generation to Die?" *The Boston Globe*, July 10, 2016, https://www.bostonglobe.com/opinion/2016/07/10/will-last-generation-die/mMmYoxmbaHsOwFjQsD7rQO/story.html.

58. Masoume Alipour, Seyed Massood Nabavi, Leila Arab, Massoud Vosough, Hossein Pakdaman, Ehsan Ehsani, and Koorosh Shahpasand, "Stem Cell Therapy in Alzheimer's Disease: Possible Benefits and Limiting Drawbacks," *Molecular Biology Reports* 46 (December 2018): 1425–46, https://doi.org/10.1007/s11033-018-4499-7.

59. Susan Blackmore, *The Meme Machine* (Oxford: Oxford University Press, 2000).

60. Wikipedia "Digital Twin" entry, accessed January 2022, https://en.wikipedia.org/wiki/Digital_twin.

61. Abhishek Kumar, "The Global Footprint of Chinese Cyber Warfare and Espionage," *Modern Diplomacy*, February 20, 2023, https://moderndiplomacy.eu/2023/02/20/the-global-footprint-of-chinese-cyber-warfare-and-espionage/.

62. Paul Voosen, "Europe Is Building a 'Digital Twin' of Earth to Revolutionize Climate Forecasts," *Science*, October 1, 2020, https://www.science.org/content/article/europe-building-digital-twin-earth-revolutionize-climate-forecasts.

63. Carl J. Öhman and David Watson, "Are the Dead Taking Over Facebook? A Big Data Approach to the Future of Death Online," *Big Data & Society* 6, no. 1 (April 2019), https://journals.sagepub.com/doi/abs/10.1177/2053951719842540.

64. Wikipedia, "Artificial intelligence" entry, accessed February 2023, https://en.wikipedia.org/wiki/Artificial_intelligence.

65. Mashrur, "Can Chess Computers Beat Humans?" *Software Chess* (blog), July 24, 2020, https://softwarechess.com/can-chess-computers-beat-humans/.

66. Rory Cellan-Jones, "Stephen Hawking Warns Artificial Intelligence Could End Mankind," BBC.com, December 2, 2014, https://www.bbc.com/news/technology-30290540.

67. Ryan Browne, "Elon Musk Warns AI Could Create an 'Immortal Dictator from which We Can Never Escape,'" CNBC.com, April 6, 2018, https://www.cnbc.com/2018/04/06/elon-musk-warns-ai-could-create-immortal-dictator-in-documentary.html.

68. Victor Tangermann, "Neuralink Co-Founder Predicts That Humanity Will Get 'Wrecked,'" *Futurism,* October 1, 2021, https://futurism.com/neuralink-cofounder-humanity-wrecked.

69. Sean Fleming, "Food Security, Cancer Research and More: Meet the People Making a Difference in Seattle and Beyond," Microsoft.com, December 1, 2020, https://news.microsoft.com/on-the-issues/2020/12/01/giving-campaign-food-security-cancer-research-housing-seattle/.

70. INNOMAG Newsroom, "Google-sjefen tror AI vil løse kreftgåten før forskerne" ["Google CEO Believes AI Will Cure Cancer before Researchers"], *INNOMAG,* April 27 2017, https://www.innomag.no/google-sjefen-tror-ai-vil-lose-kreftgaten-forskerne/.

71. Graham Phillips, "Send Robots Not People to Mars," *The Sydney Morning Herald*, November 26, 2018, https://www.smh.com.au/national/send-robots-not-people-to-mars-20181123-p50i0n.html.

72. Yuval Noah Harari, *Homo Deus: A Brief History of Tomorrow* (New York: Harper, 2017).

73. Wikipedia, "Transhumanism" entry, accessed January 2022, https://en.wikipedia.org/wiki/Transhumanism.

74. Charles Darwin, *On the Origin of Species* (London: John Murray, 1859).

About the Author

Jarle Breivik is a professor of medicine at the University of Oslo. He is an MD and has a PhD in the field of immunotherapy. His theory on the evolutionary dynamics of cancer development is presented in several high-rated medical journals and tested and confirmed by independent researchers in the *Proceedings of the National Academy of Sciences USA*. His evolutionary perspective on cancer has been featured in *Science Daily*, *WIRED*, and twice in *Scientific American*. Breivik was a Fulbright Scholar at the University of Pennsylvania, where he completed a doctorate in higher education management. He has a strong interest in science communication, and his commentaries and op-eds in the *New York Times* and other media have spurred international debate. In this book, he brings all this knowledge and experience together to present the reader with a new, insightful, and surprising understanding of cancer.

Made in the USA
Las Vegas, NV
21 November 2023

81294470R00146